The shape of things to come

Andrew Drury

ISBN 978-1-84625-707-0
Unless otherwise indicated, Scripture quotations in this publication are taken from the Holy Bible, New International Version (NIV), copyright © 1973, 1978, 1984 by International Bible Society. Used by permission of Hodder & Stoughton Publishers, a member of the Hodder Headline Group. "NIV" is a registered trademark of International Bible Society.
UK trademark number 1448790

British Library Cataloguing in Publication Data available

Published by Day One Publications
Ryelands Road, Leominster, HR6 8NZ
Telephone 01568 613 740 FAX 01568 611 473
email—sales@dayone.co.uk
website—www.dayone.co.uk

Cover design by Kathryn Chedgzoy
Printed by 4edge

4 The shape of things to come

Introduction

Obesity and being overweight is a subject that requires honesty, so we can confront the reality that putting on so much weight is an outcome of sins which are particularly prevalent in the modern era.

I know that I too have the temptation to dive into the fridge or raid the bread bin (Galatians 6:1). There are many times when I eat too much and exercise too little so, when the words that are on these pages were composed, they equally apply to me.

We can be tempted to shy away from (to use an unfortunate metaphor) the elephant in the room. The sins that cause obesity and excess weight are areas of discipleship that are overlooked or belittled by many churches—to the detriment of both the Church and, more importantly, the individual Christian. We laughingly refer to people as being 'chubby' or having 'piled on a few pounds', without really addressing what is going on in the lives of those individuals. We can even look at ourselves and joke about 'yo-yoing' as we try a diet only to put the weight back on, without referencing what harm we are doing to ourselves.

We are comfortable condemning other sins of idolatry (often citing examples that are not immediately applicable to ourselves, such as worshipping material goods or putting people on a pedestal) without realising that we too have fallen for this double sin of greed and idolatry—worshipping the food that our Maker, who gave it to us, has provided. It is out of this double sin that obesity and excess weight has arisen—the inevitable consequences of placing our desires and obsessions on things that satisfy us momentarily, rather than fixing our eyes on the Creator who supplies all good things to us.

The whole subject is not as simplistic as we would often perceive; it is not a simple equation of wrong thoughts and desires equals the accumulation of weight. There may be medical explanations why a person has excess body fat, which we will look at in the first chapter. One commentator has noted: 'I think that food is easy self-medication to help people feel good for a short time, and that actually as a society we are not dealing with stress or our mental health very well and are therefore using food and alcohol for fast injection of serotonin.'[1] For the majority, we want to fill the void in our stomachs with food that is not required to sustain us through the day.

Right from the beginning, we need to acknowledge that food is good and should never be regarded as a 'bad thing' because God never created anything bad. Indeed, in the creation of this wonderful world, He announced that all He had created was good (as seen in Genesis chapter 1). It is our misuse of His provision that has tipped it into being a problem and, in a number of incidences, a sin.

This hankering after food is not a new problem and has been going on since New Testament times (as evidenced by Paul confronting the sin in 1 Corinthians 11:21–22). Now we have the girths to prove that it is also an issue to be confronted in the present times. We claim proudly that we are walking with the Lord, yet we cannot even see our own feet, both physically and spiritually. We need to realise that to truly keep in step with the Holy Spirit, we need to throw off '... every sin that entangles us' (Hebrews 12:1), and, for many of us, it may be our super desire for food. There is not only the issue of how much is consumed (particularly in rich nations), but also the problem of the wide range of unhealthy foods (particularly those with high fat and sugar content). We will see in this publication how much of an impact these issues have in our lives. There is the truth that calls overeating, resulting in excess weight and obesity, 'the sin that the Church encourages'.

Our personal Armageddon will be fought on our waistlines as we determine who will rule over our lives—the liar who says that we need more food, or the Lord who has redeemed our fallen bodies and provided for all that we need (Matthew 6:11, 31–34). The result of our decision could lead literally to our physical deaths, but also could determine who has dominion over other aspects of our lives. We need to decide whether we will submit to how God wants us to live, given in the blueprint of Scripture, or attempt to have our own way.

We need to be convicted in our hearts that we want to follow Him resolutely or want to have avoidably shorter lives because we know God's laws but deliberately choose to disobey them.

The outcomes of being overweight and obese can be seen in medical conditions such as heart disease, strokes and diabetes, for example. It will also affect us mentally, both in the short- and the longer-term. It will rob us of joy in living and could even end in unwanted hospitalisation. It is noticeable that the scientific research that is now available has confirmed what God has been saying all the time—that the idolatry of food and greed for more, leading inevitably to gluttony, will consume you in the close. In the end, it is an evaluation as to whether we love food or we love God more, as Paul reminds us that we can be 'lovers of pleasure rather than lovers of God' (2 Timothy 3:4). In this publication, I hope to join up as many dots as possible to demonstrate that God is not a killjoy but has concern for every part of our lives.

In an age where our perspectives have been enlarged, it is beneficial to look at a wider angle because we often live with the viewpoint that we can do what we want with our bodies so long as it does not affect anyone else. The tragic truth is that the misuse and abuse of our bodies does have an effect, not only on those who live with or near us, but also to those living in other countries, which we may not have considered before. It is not something that can be localised, as obesity has become a global epidemic in addition to becoming the major contributor to the impoverishment of many people.

This book has been written mainly from a UK and western perspective, although many of the truths are to be found throughout the world. As we will observe in the chapter on obesity, there is no one nation that monopolises the impact of these sins and it is increasingly becoming a worldwide sin.

Moreover, it is an issue for you and me on a personal level. We cannot and must not sit back and think that it is for national or local governments to sort out. They are doing the best they can through healthy eating advice and encouragement to exercise (such as through the public campaigns and awareness through schools etc.), but in the end it is about personal accountability. We do not rely on governments to help us in our walk with God (thankfully), so neither should we rely on them to rectify what is, on the base level, a spiritual issue for gluttony—which can be, arguably, termed the Christian's favourite sin.

Our hospital beds are full of people living with the consequences of bad diets and little, or no, exercise. It is no wonder that our prayer requests in our fellowships grow as we defy our Maker's instructions and more people we know (or it could even be ourselves) end up in these medical facilities. When we hear of people who are hospitalised, it is a sobering thought that many of these conditions have been caused by a combination of poor diet and little exercise, whether in the past and/or in the present time.

The story is told of a preacher, Charles Lowery, complaining to his friend about lower back pain that he was experiencing. He was expecting words of sympathy, but he got an honest assessment in response. His friend told him bluntly: 'I don't think your back pain is your problem; it's your stomach. Your stomach is pulling on your back.' Charles was wise enough to resist the temptation to be offended, so he lost the weight and the back problem went away.'[2]

It could be that, after reading this book, you might feel you do not need to lose weight, but it could be that you could exercise more, have a lifestyle change, resolve to submit to the spiritual discipline of fasting or another issue addressed in this book is required. It would be an encouragement to know that we, who want to reflect our Heavenly King, are taking His words seriously and that this aspect of our lives is in line with how He wants us to live. We cannot be complacent as the pounds/kilograms will easily pile onto the waistline—we need to prevent ourselves from being overweight, let alone from being obese—so we need to prevent the blunting of our mental states and the adverse impact on our lifestyle.

We are reminded that: 'Better is open rebuke than hidden love. Wounds from a friend can be trusted, but an enemy multiplies kisses.' (Proverbs 27:5–6). I trust that you will read this book as coming from a friend, who hopes that you will enjoy all that God has made in you by following His instructions as He knows best.

I hope that you will make that voyage to a God-given, healthy lifestyle with me.

NOTES

1   E-mail from Jonathan Martin to author, 13 February 2020
2   Poh Fang Chia, 'Wounds from a friend', *Our Daily Journey*, (Grand Rapids, Michigan: Our Daily Bread Ministries, 10 December 2017)

1 Obesity

You shall have no other gods before me (Exodus 20:3,
Deuteronomy 5:7).

The seed that fell among thorns stands for those who hear, but as
they go on their way they are choked by life's worries, riches and
pleasures, and they do not mature (Luke 8:14).

What is obesity?

What we can observe is that, with very few medical
exceptions, the vast majority of people in the world who
are obese or overweight are so by choosing unhealthy
options, even to the point of picking at a packet of snacks here and a
bar of chocolate there, without any exercise being undertaken. On a
personal basis, I find the lure of an opened box of chocolates too
appealing on occasions to throw me off course from my game plan
of only having one in an evening.

Often, it is the subconscious mind that makes these choices—
possibly out of boredom, a lack of sleep, feeling depressed or any
number of other factors. It seems as though our fingers can go
walking through our fridges, biscuit barrels or bread bins without
any thought being applied. With each amount of food that our body
does not require and the lack of physical activity that it should have,
the weight will almost inevitably accumulate, unless we have a very
active metabolism, which only a small minority of younger people
seem to possess.

Before we proceed, we have to acknowledge that there are a

number of factors that increase the risk of obesity or excess weight that could include: genetics; epigenetics; neurohormonal mechanisms; associated chronic diseases and obesogenic medications; sociocultural practices and beliefs (like the belief that it shows wealth to be able to afford to eat excessively); social determinants of health; built environment; individual life experiences like adverse childhoods; and many psychological factors. It could simply be the onset of the menopause for women, where the reduction of oestrogen means that weight is added.

Other examples of physical factors in the medical sphere could include those people who have, for example, problems with their thyroids, where medical intervention (such as prescription drugs) would be necessary.

Another possible exception is that of people living with mental health issues. An example of this factor is the eating disorders experienced by people living with autism. People on the autism spectrum are more likely to have eating disorders that are more severe and longer lasting, to the effect that they are more likely to die one to three decades earlier, on average, than those not on the autism spectrum. It is caused by their cognitive rigidity that entraps them into patterns of eating behaviour, while their preference for the familiar will limit them to the same foods, which often includes sugary and low nutritional meals. For some people on the autistic spectrum, there might be also an insensitivity to hunger, gastrointestinal problems and sensitivity to tastes, smells and textures.

In the medical sphere, both mental and physical, the causes of obesity and excess weight are more complex than it is often perceived. However, for the majority of us (including myself), excess weight is a clear outcome of placing food and satisfaction (greed and idolatry) on a higher level in our lives than it should be— even to the point of supplanting our need for God.

We can try to explain it away as something other than what it clearly is. We try to wiggle out by making excuses, such as inherited factors. Unfortunately, the claim to have 'big bones' or that it 'runs in the family' is not scientifically substantiated, but more commonly it is the result of unhealthy eating and exercise.

No one ever got fat by eating too much celery!

The definition of obesity

A recent definition of obesity is 'a prevalent, complex, progressive, and relapsing chronic disease, characterized by abnormal or excessive body fat (adiposity) that impairs health'.[1]

We might prefer the easier definition that obesity is when a person's body weight is at least 20 per cent greater than it should be according to the height and weight tables, such as the commonly used BMI (Body Mass Index) (see Appendix A, p. 310). Admittedly, it is not fool proof as it can show a muscular person as being overweight/obese since muscles are denser in weight than fat. However, the BMI is a fairly good indicator that we can subjectively rely on, although the waist/hip circumference ratio* is a better way of measurement.

There must be an awareness of the difference between being

*The waist/hip circumference ratio is calculated as waist measurement divided by hip measurement. For example, a person who has a 30-inch (78 cm) waist and a 38-inch hip has a waist/hip ratio of approximately 0.78. The World Health Organisation has stated that women with >0.85 and men with >0.90 ratios fall within the obese category.

obese and being overweight, although the latter can easily be a step towards the former, with a threshold that can be stepped over without any indication whatsoever. There are no amber or red warning lights that flash before our eyes—we can transform into being overweight or obese with only signs being around our bellies as our trousers or skirts get too tight. There can be no smugness if we find ourselves only in the overweight category as the impact of this state can, as we shall see, still be detrimental to our physical and mental health.

In order to see whether we are obese or overweight, we can helpfully use the scales that are commonly found in many homes (to determine our weight) and a measuring stick or other ruler (to determine our height) so we can observe if we are the correct weight for how tall (or short) we are. Another method we can utilise is to use callipers and a body fat scale which runs electrical currents through the body to indicate how much body fat we have.

You might find it helpful to weigh yourself daily, although the stress of doing that everyday might cause you stress and the resultant raised cortisol will retain the body weight. The accepted advice is that weighing-in on a weekly basis will be enough. However, it is important not to be too disheartened since there will be fluctuations as your body retains fat before eventually releasing it.

It has been suggested that the 'eyeball' test is better—if a person looks overweight, then that person is overweight. However, it is easy to be judgemental in pronouncing that the other person is overweight or obese when you have a substantial weight problem yourself (Matthew 7:3–5).

We must acknowledge that, once a person has started to put on the weight, it can be very difficult to take it off. Obesity has been described as 'a chronic condition, resistant to treatment, and prone to relapse'.[2] It is only with support from friends and family, advice from professional organisations, medical intervention (in extreme cases), a determination to follow God's way and, most importantly, reliance on God Himself, that this consequence of sin can be overcome.

Death due to obesity and overweight

Of the 4 million deaths worldwide attributed to excessive weight in 2015,[3] 40 per cent fell below the obesity threshold, so highlighting the fact that it is more than just a matter of being obese—being overweight, however slightly, can equally be detrimental to life. The impact of excess fat, regardless of how much there is, will be detrimental to our physical wellbeing, however much we would like to think otherwise.

It is a global problem, as it has been estimated that 10 per cent of the world's population has a Body Mass Index (BMI) of 30 or higher. Part of the problem has been identified as when a nation obtains more wealth, its population becomes more attracted to fast food.[4]

There are situations where, although the poorer sectors of society have more money than previous generations, they are still unable to purchase healthy food (which often comes as a cost beyond their means), and so they resort to purchasing cheaper meals that these fast-food outlets sell—it is noticeable that it is those people in the lower socio-economic groups that are more adversely affected than those in the higher sectors. Regardless of the actions of this sector to try and introduce healthier options, part of the problem is that, as we as a society become richer, there is less time in our increasingly stressful lives to look after our bodies. This could lead to laziness in our preparation of good food, and so we fall back on our default position of purchasing food that is invariably higher in salt, sugar and fat.

Furthermore, the consequences of obesity are increased by not enough or no exercise, with most people preferring to sit in the comfort of their armchairs rather than taking on activities which could, in all probability, extend their lives, contribute to physical wellbeing and promote good mental health. We live in an increasingly sedentary society where we drive our cars or go on public transport rather than walking long distances; we are on chairs for most of our working hours; we are in seats during our recreation hours (such as watching sport, a film or the television); and even spend much of our time at church being seated.

The marginalization of healthy food is an increasing possibility as it is easier to delve into the fridge or the freezer after a hectic day and pull out a packaged meal, that would be ready in a few minutes after being heated in the microwave—especially if there was no or little washing up at the end of the process—than to prepare a nutritious meal with fresh or frozen vegetables, accompanied with the inevitable cleaning of the pots and pans. It is often easier to peel back the top off a carton or to pierce the clingfilm than to peel a carrot or even to heat up peas in a saucepan. The result of the reliance on fast and convenience foods could be that we will be observing the highest death rate of a younger generation since the First World War.

The size of the problem

The World Health Organisation (WHO) has calculated that, in 2016, there were over 1.9 billion people (18 years and over) who were overweight/obese, which meant 39 per cent of all adults (39 per cent of men and 40 per cent of women) were overweight and 13 per cent of all adults (11 per cent of men and 15 per cent of women) were obese—tripling the figures since 1975.[5] As more current statistics become available, there is a sad inevitability that the statistics will worsen, unless we all seek to reverse the situation.

It is ironic that most of the world's population live in nations where the conditions of being overweight and obese kill more people than being underweight. It is an indictment of us as human beings that we have gobbled up the world's resources and left so little for the defenceless and oppressed. In global terms, it is true of every region except sections of sub-Saharan Africa and Asia, where exploitation of people is also prevalent. We march and fundraise for the people who are hungry, but paradoxically we also use up the natural resources that they rely on, because we insist on our food and other goods being available for purchase cheaply and all of the year round. We shall look later on how, through wanting resources at cut prices, we exploit them. We can be regarded as people who are '... foolish, disobedient, deceived and enslaved by all kinds of passions and pleasures' (Titus 3:3).

We have been warned of the consequences through the words of the prophet Isaiah: 'The Lord, the LORD Almighty, called you on that day to weep and to wail, to tear out your hair and put on sackcloth. But see, there is joy and revelry, slaughtering of cattle and killing of sheep, eating of meat and drinking of wine! "Let us eat and drink", you say, "for tomorrow we die!" The LORD Almighty has revealed this in my hearing: "Till your dying day, this sin will not be atoned for", says the LORD Almighty' (Isaiah 22:12–14).

We cannot see the irony and disconnect of what we do and what we proclaim—there is a disharmony between our words and our actions. An example would be the increasingly vocal protestation, correctly, at how we are abusing the planet, especially resulting in environmental change. However, we cannot march with paunched stomachs and claim that we are not harming our environment, for we will be contributing to the epidemic of obesity (the abuse of this world and the situation of obesity are intrinsically intertwined, as we shall see later in the book). The cheap burgers bought during a protest at the ravaging of the world's resources, will have been obtained at the probable cost of the loss of rainforest habitat.

Through our actions, we do see the picture of increasing obesity across the world, as the phenomenon has meant that it has doubled in more than seventy countries in twenty-five years.[6]

The reality is that, in real terms, it does not matter about the percentages, as most nations are experiencing the epidemic of obesity. The tsunami of obesity is gradually reaching into all parts of the world, gradually corrupting what God saw as being good when He created it.

On the global scale, the World Health Organisation (WHO)[7] defined the fundamental cause of obesity and overweight as being the energy imbalance between the calories consumed and the calories expended. The WHO report indicated clearly that there were two major contributory factors, namely:

a) the increased intake of energy-dense foods that are high in fat (such as those found in many fast and convenience foods)

b) an increase in physical inactivity due to the increased sedentary nature of most forms of work, changing modes of transport, and increasing urbanisation.

Simply put, as found in the vast majority of cultures in the world, we are eating too much and exercising too little.

Interlinking factors

The WHO report recognised that the improvements in diet and physical activity are often resulting from environmental and societal development changes. These changes can also be accompanied by supportive policies in areas such as health, agriculture (how our food is produced), transport (how we can travel in a way that gives us exercise and supports the climate), urban planning (how we live will incentivise healthy living), environment (which is addressed later in the book), food processing (how we can live with less salt and sugar), marketing (how we can be aware of the contents of products) and education (how we can learn to eat more healthily). We need linked-up policies that address the issue of obesity and not leave it to one government department (and it is usually the one that majors on health).

We need organisations from across many subject areas to work together, which is why I support organisations like Tearfund and Oxfam in their work. There is a need to join these aspects of our body health together with environmental and social issues so that there is a more holistic approach, where God's people could and should join in—as we should be looking at the larger picture.

Obesity and poverty

We must be concerned that, ironically, in low- and middle-income countries, there is a 'double burden' of disease. Whilst there are problems with malnutrition and infectious diseases in these nations, there is also a rapid increase in noncommunicable disease risk factors (such as obesity and excess weight), particularly in the urban areas. It is common to find undernutrition and obesity side-by-side within the same country, the same community and even the same household. Neighbourhoods can be filled with those who are obese or overweight living cheek by jowl with those who are starving because they are unable to buy even the most rudimentary of foodstuffs.

The dichotomy can be explained in part by the ease and cheapness of convenience foods compared to the provision of fresh food. However, sadly, there are regions where not even the locality of a bargain supermarket means that the nearby inhabitants have access to food, as it might still be out of their price range.

There is a delicious irony that if a person or family are in such dire straits that they require handouts from such organisations as foodbanks, they might receive food that is more nutritious than had they got enough money to buy from fast-food outlets.

Regardless of our place in the socio-economic structure, we need to be alert to the fact that obesity and being overweight is an increasing consequence of the double sin that is engulfing the world and, unless we see it from God's perspective, there will be no receding of the tide of obesity that threatens to drag us under.

ACTION POINTS

- *Consider gluttony as evidenced by obesity and being overweight as a sin. Confess this sin before God and ask Him to remove this idol from your life.*
- *Weigh yourself on a weekly basis and keep a written record.*
- *Look at the food and drink in your freezer/fridge/larder— consider what you could remove in order to live a healthier life.*

NOTES

1 Sean Wharton et al, 'Obesity in adults: a clinical practice guideline', *Canadian Medical Association Journal*, 4 August 2020, 192 (31): E875–E891 https://www.cmaj.ca/content/192/31/E875#sec-26

2 Albert J Stankard, 'Obesity' in *Comprehensive Textbook of Psychiatry/IV*, ed. Harold I Kaplin and Benjamin J Sadock (Baltimore: Williams & Wilkins, 1985), p. 1138

3 Cited in 'Being overweight, not even obese, can kill', The Metro, 13 June 2017

4 Dionne Searcey and Matt Richtel, 'Obesity Was Rising as Ghana Embraced Fast Food. Then Came KFC', *New York Times*, 2 October 2017 https://www.nytimes.com/2017/10/02/health/ghana-kfc-obesity.html

5 'Obesity and overweight', World Health Organisation, updated October 2017 http://www.who.int/mediacentre/factsheets/fs311/en/

6 The GB 2015 Obesity Collaborators, 'Health Effects of Overweight and Obesity in 195 Countries over 25 Years', *New England Journal of Medicine*, 6 July 2017, issue 377, pp. 13–27, http://www.nejm.org/doi/full/10.1056/NEJMoa1614362

7 Obesity and overweight, World Health Organisation, updated October 2017 http://www.who.int/mediacentre/factsheets/fs311/en/

2 The physical impact of obesity

> Ehud reached with his left hand, drew the sword from his right thigh and plunged it into the king's belly. Even the handle sank in after the blade, which came out of his back. Ehud did not pull his sword out, and the fat closed in over it (Judges 3:21–22).

A judge in early Israelite history, Ehud, took on the king of Moab in his own palace. The king's unwise decisions included not having a total body check of Ehud to ensure that there were no weapons on his person and also to be totally absorbed in affluent living.

One of the lessons we can learn from this king is that, although our body fat will (hopefully) not determine that we will be killed by a sword, there are other implications that will shorten our lives. If the king had been more prudent as to what he ate and undertaken more exercise, he could have had the ability to get away from danger and he would certainly have been less of a target for his assailant—who knows, he might have survived the assassination attempt.

In a similar way, as we look at what is happening to our girths in the modern world, we need to be aware that, as the researchers have determined, the raised BMI in overweight and obese people is a major risk factor for noncommunicable diseases, some of which are detailed below. We can eat healthier and exercise more so that we dodge the metaphorical sword that is heading our way.

Throughout the world, it was ascertained that *cardiovascular diseases* (mainly heart disease and stroke) brought on by obesity and excess weight is the major cause of death.[1]

Type 2 diabetes, brought on by obesity and excess weight, was another condition that resulted not only in increased mortality, but also in impaired mobility and other lifestyle restrictions.

Obesity and excess weight also resulted in *musculoskeletal disorders* (especially osteoarthritis—a disabling degenerative joint disease), which again resulted in impaired mobility and other restrictions to a person's lifestyle.

There was an increase in *some cancers* (including endometrial, breast, ovarian, prostate, liver, gallbladder, kidney and colon) that were known to have increased risk factors as a result of obesity.

THE NUMBER OF PREDICTED NEW CASES OF CHRONIC ILLNESSES CAUSED BY OBESITY IN THE 36 COUNTRIES OF THE ORGANISATION FOR ECONOMIC CO-OPERATION AND DEVELOPMENT (OECD), 2020–2050[2]		
Outcomes	**Number of cases**	**Percentage of total cases**
Cardio Vascular Diseases (CVD)	462,099.034	18%
Diabetes	212,433,543	58%
Dementia	30,957,527	11%
Cancers	16,649,622	8%
Cirrhosis	-2,772,673	-6%
Injuries	-20,432,751	-3%
Chronic Obstructive Pulmonary Diseases (COPD)	-31,717,576	-6%

We shall look at these effects in greater detail later, but already it can be observed what consequences can occur.

There is no getting away from the unavoidable fact, which is staring us in the face, that the risk for these diseases increases with every increase in the BMI. Every ounce/gram that is stockpiled on the body is another notch up the risk scale of us being impacted by one or more of these conditions, and every 4 inches/10 cm added to the circumference of the waist increases the risk of dying prematurely from all causes by 11 percent.[3] Every inch that you pinch is another rise in your risk.

An example is an observation from research undertaken on men, that discovered there was not an increase in mortality if the fat was spread around the body. However, for men in particular, most of the fat tends to congregate dangerously in the belly where it coats the vital organs, such as the liver, pancreas and intestines. There is a warning as this could interfere with the normal functions of those organs and promote the growth of cancerous cells. In some cases, there was a 35 per cent increased risk of earlier morbidity for those who are obese and have prostate cancer.[4]

It is also hazardous to our health to not only be obese but be merely overweight—although we often tell ourselves the comforting lie that we have put just a little weight on. Of the 4 million deaths in the world attributed to people being overweight, including those involving Type 2 diabetes, heart disease and some cancers, almost 40 per cent were not perceived to be obese.

Regardless of which country we are from, it is true that being overweight is a major contributor to preventative death and can raise morbidity risks associated with chronic diseases such as hypertension, stroke, respiratory problems and various cancers.

Evidence by MRI

It is amazing how MRI (magnetic resonance imaging) scans have increased our knowledge of the impact of obesity. We can observe the harm that we are doing to our bodies, as we cram harmful fats and sugars into our stomachs, by looking at these images.

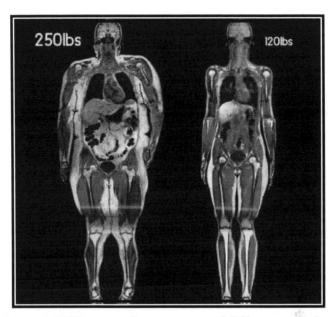

Figure 1: MRI scans of two women of different weights.

Fig 1 is a clear demonstration of how body fat affects our bone and muscle structure.[5] The woman on the left is 5'6" (1.7 m) tall, weighs 250 pounds (17 stone 8 lb, 113 kg), and has a BMI of 40.3, so she is classified as morbidly obese. The woman on the right is 5'5" tall (1.7 m), weighs 120 pounds (8 stone 6 lb, 55 kg) and has a BMI of 20 (a healthy BMI is considered to be between 18.5 and 24.9).

The ankles of the woman on the left are deformed as she is effectively carrying another person in her body for the extra weight is bearing down on her musculoskeletal system. Her knee joints have to deal with the additional load, which will expedite the onset of osteoarthritis in those joints, and her ankles are suffering irreparable harm, which will affect the way that she walks, with the complication of affecting her spine as her body seeks to readjust to her steps.

The fat around her spine and the core muscles will result in increased instances of back ache, which could result in numerous other complications. It could end up leading to referrals to osteopaths and physiotherapists to rectify the painful consequences.

She is likely to experience immobility caused by the increased body mass. She will have difficulty in walking and so will have to resort in the long term (especially if the weight increase continues) to mobility aids (such as walking sticks, Zimmer frames and mobility vehicles). In addition, there is the compression of her internal organs as the fat surrounds her heart and other vital components of her body.

It is a salutary warning that we need to consider how we treat our bodies, as demonstrated by the MRI scans on these two women.

Social implications

Research on British social attitudes concluded that people tend to overestimate what obesity means in terms of body size.[6] When they look at themselves in the mirror, people tend to see that they 'have put on a bit of weight' without realising that the truth is they are obese. The clue might be in the number of clothes sold in sizes with

X in the classification having gone up, so it not only includes XL (extra-large) but goes up to XXXL (extra-extra-extra-large).

As far as fashion sizes are concerned, in women's clothing, there has been the controversy of models being the American size 0, and yet there seems to be the normalization of sizes up to 20 and beyond, with particular brands and stores being targeted for the 'larger lady'. It has become normalized to offer sizes of merchandise that would have been unthought of in years gone by, as people in the past were generally slimmer due to healthier diets and more active lifestyles.

Being calorie aware

In a National Geographical article, Lawrence Cheskin, the director of the John Hopkins Weight Management Centre, stated the First Law of Fat, which is that anything you eat beyond your immediate need for energy, from avocados to ziti (so that includes anything which is regarded as healthy foods), converts to fat. He commented that, 'a calorie is a calorie is a calorie', regardless of whether it comes in the form of fat, protein or carbohydrate.

The Second Law of Fat is that the line between being in and out of the energy balance is narrow. The example was given of being 5 per cent over the 2,000 calorie-a-day average. The response from Rudolph Leibel, the head of molecular genetics at Columbia university, is: 'That's just 100 calories; it's a glass of apple juice. But those few extra calories can mean a huge weight gain.'[7]

The calculation is that, since one pound (0.45 kg) of body weight is almost equivalent to 3,500 calories, the glass of apple juice adds up to an extra 10 pounds (5 kg) over the duration of a year. Another way of looking at it is that you could gain that same 10 pounds (5 kg) if you adopt a more sedentary lifestyle and so not burn 100 calories a day.

We tend not to think of how much we eat, especially as we put hand to mouth mindlessly while watching television. It is an easy temptation to put our hands into the dish of snacks in front of us whilst we are engrossed in the latest blockbuster, video game or absorbing television programme. It is easy to add to our calorie intake without any thought being given to our actions and their consequences. We think, especially at the end of a gruelling day or week, that we deserve an unhealthy treat, but the constant pick-me-ups soon develop into an unhealthy diet.

Hospital admissions

Within a four-year period when the rate of obesity had doubled in England, it was calculated that there were nearly 617,000 hospital admissions in 2016–17 where obesity was the primary or secondary cause. This was an increase from 292,000 in 2012–13. By definition, the primary diagnosis included weight-loss treatments, while secondary diagnoses included hip problems, heart attacks and strokes.

The main cause in 10,705 admissions was obesity, which was an increase of 8 per cent over the previous year. Meanwhile, bariatric surgery appointments (that is the treatment of obesity) rose to 6,760, which was an increase of 5 per cent over the same timeframe.

Regarding age groups, it was the 35- to 64-year-olds who constituted 69 per cent of the admissions. As to gender, women attended 66 per cent of all obesity-related appointments and experienced 77 per cent of bariatric surgeries.[8]

These surgeries can vary but they can include reducing the size of the stomach by inserting a gastric band, removal of the stomach, or rerouting the small intestine to a small stomach pouch.

These admissions are largely avoidable as many people were, on the whole (bearing in mind what we have already observed, that it could be through a number of factors), responsible for their own weight gain, so they cannot blame the government, society or any other organisation—people were not forced to eat the food. In the United Kingdom, many of the major food suppliers and sellers outline the contents of the food on the packages (particularly with regard to fat, sugar, salt and calorie information), although the labelling system is constantly being looked at to see if it can be improved. There are also health awareness campaigns being conducted by national and local government, and other organisations. People are being educated so that they have opportunities to avoid such admissions to hospital.

In the recent Covid-19 pandemic, it was noticed that many of those patients, who were affected more severely and needed hospitalisation, were obese or had underlying conditions exacerbated or caused by obesity. 'The authors of the study reported: 'At a BMI of more than 23 kg/m2, we found a linear increase in the risk of severe Covid-19 leading to admission to hospital and death.' Their observation might indicate an underlying biological association between increasing weight and risk of severe Covid-19.[9] They continued: 'Since over two-thirds of westernized society are overweight or obese, this potentially presents a major risk factor for severe Covid-19 infection and may have implications for policy.'[10] Indeed, the effects of Long-Covid (where the symptoms such as extreme fatigue exist after three months from diagnosis) has been made worse by obesity and overweight.

The increased number of people hospitalized together with their expanded lengths of stays, whether during a pandemic or not, adds extra strain on the individual (with regard to stress and possible consequences of operations, for instance), their families (with worry), and the health service (with manpower and finance). In the worst scenarios, the admission of a person into hospital could end up with long-term outcomes (as with Long-Covid), admittance to a care home or respite centre, or (at the very worst) death. The most depressing part about it is that the situation could have been (by and large) avoided if the person had taken steps (both figuratively and literally) to eat healthily and to take exercise, so that being obese or overweight was no longer a possibility.

The knock-on effect of the increased hospitalization of obese and overweight people is that the national insurance contributions in the United Kingdom to pay for the public healthcare are increased. The time spent by doctors, nurses and administrative staff in dealing with such issues could be better utilized in areas where the circumstances are not contributed to by the patient (such as conditions caused by genetic factors) and money spent on resources such as beds and mobility aids could be diverted to other hospital needs and research.

In other countries, where there is no public health service, there is the increase in health insurance premiums that can be reduced if overeating is avoided.

OBESITY AND THE ECONOMIC BURDEN [11] % OF ESTIMATED HEALTH EXPENDITURE SPENT ON OVERWEIGHT AND RELATED CONDITIONS 2020–2050	
France	5%
Japan	6%
United Kingdom	8%
OECD average	8.4%
Italy	9%
Canada	11%
Germany	11%
United States	14%

Living unhealthy lifestyles

A study has shown that the majority of adults in England were so unhealthy that they put their lives at risk—a situation that is not unique to that country. It was ascertained that half of all adults in England have two or more of the following risk factors: smoking, drinking more than 14 units of alcohol, eating fewer than five portions of fruit and vegetables, are obese or have low rates of physical activity. It is a country looking for a heart attack, although (as we keep stating) it is a global epidemic.

One of the noticeable signs of how obesity and excess weight is affecting us is to notice how fast people in their 40+ age group walk, which is an indicator of their future physical and mental health. It was noticeable among the overweight walkers that not only do the bodies age more quickly, but their faces looked older and their brains were smaller. The latter indicator would be linked to a higher risk of dementia and decline.[12]

UNHEALTHY DIETS AND LACK OF PHYSICAL ACTIVITY UNDERPIN THE RISE IN BEING OVERWEIGHT[13]	
50% of people have an unhealthy diet (measured against national guidelines)	40% of waking time is spent in sedentary activities (e.g. watching TV)
1 in 3 people do not do a sufficient amount of physical activity	2 in 5 individuals do not consume a sufficient amount of fruit and vegetables

Unusually, the survey compared the lifestyles of children with their parents. The possible connection was made that children with obese parents were approximately three times more likely to be obese than children whose parents were of a healthy weight.[14]

It was calculated that 28 per cent of children of obese mothers were also obese compared with 8 per cent of children whose mothers were of a healthy weight. Likewise, 24 per cent of children of obese fathers were also obese compared with 9 per cent of children whose fathers were a healthy weight.

We can see that learnt behaviour is a major contributor to the problem. Although there could be a link between nurture and nature, it is the former that is predominant, as genes play a minute part in this scenario. What a child observes in the adult responsible for them, they are more likely to copy, even if it is detrimental to them, like eating badly and having little or no physical activity.

Michael Pearl has helpfully commented: 'Everything a child experiences, either by way of indulgence or the self-restraint you impose, is preparing him [or her] for the day when he [or she] matures into a responsible, moral soul. Somewhere on that road of development, each child will graduate to commence his [or her] full accountability. That child then stands alone before God, without excuse. It becomes his [or her] day of accountability.'[15]

The Bible has given us pertinent instruction such as: 'Train [or start] a child in the way he should go, and when he is old, he will not turn from it' (Proverbs 22:6). As adults, we have a duty to follow the guidance in Scripture to live the healthy lifestyle that God has ordained and then to model it for the next generation.

Genetics

Despite the protestation by people that they cannot help being obese or overweight because of their genes, research has shown that a person's genetic composition does not play a major part in their body's ability to lose or gain weight. It was ascertained that environmental factors are likely to have a greater impact.

In looking at the gut processes, only 17.9 per cent of obesity could be attributed to heredity factors, whereas 67.7 per cent were attributed to environmental factors such as an individual's diet.[16]

It is like any other temptation when we like to blame someone else, as was exhibited by Adam and Eve in the Garden of Eden who both shifted blame onto the next person—only in this case it is us, as we blame our chromosomes when we reach out for another cream cake. We have to realise that we have a personal responsibility for our own bodies before God.

When we have the urge to overindulge—to give in to the dual sins of greed and idolatry—we are to remember that God wants us to live for Him in a healthy and sustainable way. He reminds us: 'Be careful, or you will be enticed to turn away and worship other gods and bow down to them' (Deuteronomy 11:16). It is not money or any other material items, but food that can so often be the easiest and most accessible thing that we can place in our hearts as first importance over God. Indeed, He proclaims: 'I am the LORD; that is my name! I will not give my glory to another or my praise to idols' (Isaiah 42:8). We need to constantly remind ourselves as to Who gave us the food—looking beyond the plate to the Provider.

Overeating

It is evident every Christmas that there is a problem in the UK and in the western world with the excess food that will be consumed. Every year, I go into the local supermarkets and notice the mounds of food and drink piled up so that it overflows from the shelves onto the floors and it makes me wonder who is going to consume all of this! There is enough food and drink in that one festive season to supply a small nation for a year.

Even at pre-Christmas events, it was expected that 4,941 calories will be consumed by an average person over the period of attending pre-festive meals and snacks, which is the equivalent of 255 million Christmas dinners throughout the UK. This figure excludes the additional 2,000 calories included in the food and drink that would be eaten and imbibed throughout the actual day.

In addition, people in the UK spend nearly 10 billion hours sitting down over the festive period in December and would have weighed an additional 19.5 billion stone as a result.

One-third (33 per cent) of people also admit to having done absolutely no exercise during that month, while a further 33 per cent would have done less than an hour a week.[17]

It is not only the Christmas period that sees the money being splashed out on groceries, and other food and drink. There are many other religious and cultural settings (both on a national level such as Thanksgiving Day or Easter, or locally such as a church anniversary) where the food is piled up metaphorically to the ceiling. There needs to be the discernment as to when the line is crossed from hospitality to greed.

In the midst of celebrations and meeting up, we need to ask questions to maintain a healthy lifestyle, such as: 'Do I really need three courses? What are the choices on the menu that will help me get to or keep in good physical shape?'

Going for the wrong options

It is a sad indication that statistics have shown that the younger generations are not opting for fresh fruit but opting for ready-packaged alternatives instead.

A study has indicated that young adults aged between 16 and 24 years are more likely to depend on convenience foods, which are often high in fat and sugar, compared to those people aged 65 years and over. In context, 79 million ready meals and 22 million fast-food and takeaway meals were purchased in one week in the UK by all age groups. Between the genders, men were more likely to consume convenience foods than women.[18] It is easier to pick up something from the 'on the move' section in the supermarket where the only preparation is to pierce the plastic before putting the container in the microwave.

It is not unusual for people to be eating such 'TV meals' (typically ready meals that are full of salt, sugar and the wrong types of fat) while, ironically, watching TV cookery shows that demonstrate how you can eat wholesome foods. It can be said that, in fairness, many of the television channels are promoting better ways of eating and drinking that would not abuse our bodies.

When not in front of their screens, today's children and young people spend more than twice as much time eating out in restaurants and fast-food outlets than previous generations (certainly comparing the situation today with the 1970s), treating such occasions as a major part of their weekly diet. I remember the days of the 1970s and 1980s when going out for a meal was a special treat (such as for significant birthdays or other life events), whereas even I have eaten out more recently on a whim (although we have become more aware and so reduced our visits to restaurants and tried to consume more nutritiously home-cooked food). Research has shown that, in a given week in 2017 in England, 75 per cent of people had eaten out or had ordered a takeaway. In addition, it has been estimated that one in five families have at least two takeaways a week.[19]

It is a worrying trend, as people who eat out regularly are at greater risk of being overweight and, therefore, developing Type 2 diabetes compared to those who ate at home. There is little problem if people go to a fast-food restaurant a maximum of once a week as a 'treat', but it is when it is more regular that it becomes a matter of concern. (Incidentally, it has to be recognised that there are restaurants that are providing healthier options, such as for vegan and vegetarian customers, or meals that are routinely smaller in portion size.) It seems paradoxical that we can go to church buildings to praise the Creator who made all things good and then assemble in a fast-food outlet that abuses our bodies—one of the good, created things that we manage to damage with our sinful behaviour.

It is recommended that parents or other responsible adults help children to order healthy food off the menu, especially when the calorific values were shown, in order to minimise the impact on their developing bodies. It is true that every day we are assaulted visually by the lure of cheap, high-calorie food and drinks, for what we see in the media, in our shops and on the street encourages us to consume too much.

The worries of Dr Alison Tedstone, the Public Health England (PHE) chief nutritionist, are being realised as she commented: 'Children on average have three meals from the "out of home" sector [restaurants, takeaways and fast-food outlets] every week. That's a lot of calories.'[20]

Socio-economic distinctions

With one in four adults in Britain now being classified as obese, it is people from lower socio-economic groups who are less likely to be healthy, both in terms of diet and exercise, than those from higher socio-economic groups.

It was observed that obesity affected only 16 per cent of higher managerial and professional women while 20 per cent of lower managerial and professional women were obese.[21]

We are not being advocates for the powerless if we do not seek to change the situation. We should strive, by lobbying or any other means obtainable, to ensure that those who are materially impoverished are not further damaged by food choices that they do not have the power to change due to the impact of increased stress found in daily life and the monetary inability to purchase more healthy options, for example.

It is the role of the Church to help all who are in those lower socio-economic groups. We are called to carry on doing good, especially (but not exclusively) for fellow Christians. It can be that the lost art of hospitality in the local church can help in the encouragement of one another to eat healthily and to support those who are not financially able to purchase fresh fruit and vegetables (which can be prohibitively expensive for those on state aid).

People living in the poorer socio-economic groups are more likely to be impacted by obesity and excess weight, so we should be supporting initiatives like the foodbanks. The Bible encourages us to be open-hearted and open-handed: 'If there is a poor man among your brothers in any of the towns of the land that the LORD your God is giving you, do not be hard-hearted or tight-fisted towards your poor brother.' (Deuteronomy 15:7) There is blessing in helping those people living in poverty: 'Blessed is he who has regard for the weak; the LORD delivers him in times of trouble' (Psalm 41:1), and '... blessed is he who is kind to the needy' (Proverbs 14:21).

The same sentiment was expressed by Jesus when He told the rich young man, 'If you want to be perfect, go, sell your possessions and give to the poor, and you will have treasure in heaven' (Matthew 19:21).

In addition, Paul was asked to remember the poor by the other apostles as he set out in his ministry. He remarked that it was the very thing that he was keen to do (Galatians 2:10).

It is important that we follow the early Church in devoting ourselves to the fellowship (Acts 2:42) so that our brothers and sisters in the Lord can have access to the good things that the Lord provides, both spiritually and physically.

On a diet

In the United Kingdom, it was reported in 2018 that the nation was being 'put on a diet' as the fast-food chains were ordered to 'calorie cap' the meals that were being given out to customers.

In an edict, Public Health England (PHE) ordered fast-food chains and the suppliers of supermarket ready meals to reduce the calories in lunches and dinners to 600 calories.

An example was given that a box meal from KFC (Kentucky Fried Chicken) had a calorific value of 1,400, and a big Mac and regular fries had 845 at the time of the directive. Although these chains were named and shamed, there were many other examples of calorie-filled meals. The statistics showed that consumers of such meals ate 200–300 more calories per day than they should.[22]

The increase of obesity and being overweight

There has been an increase over time as, in the UK, approximately 40 per cent of the population were overweight and less than 10 per cent were obese in the 1980s; the situation today is that two-thirds of adults are overweight and more than a fifth are obese. These statistics are reflected in the increase in the risk of the associated conditions of hypertension, Type 2 diabetes, cardiovascular disease, gall bladder disease and some cancers.

In stark terms, in 2008, around 10 million adults aged 16 years and over (24.5 per cent) were obese, up from 14.9 per cent in 1993. Of these people, 80,000 (2.0 per cent) were morbidly obese. More startlingly, approximately 1.4 million children aged 2–15 years (16.0 per cent) were obese, a rise from 11.7 per cent in 1995.[23]

The occurrence of obesity in the United Kingdom was 27 per cent in 2017. This was far higher than the average for the OECD (Organisation for Economic Development) countries which was 19 per cent in the same year. The UK was cited as one of the five countries having a 'historically high' rate of obesity since the 1990s, with an increase rate of 92 per cent compared to 65 per cent in the United States[24]. The lessons are to be learnt from countries such as Canada and Australia whose obesity levels were reduced and stabilised by healthy eating and exercise, and with Japan's rate being the lowest at 4 per cent.[25]

A 20% REDUCTION OF CALORIE CONTENT IN ENERGY-DENSE FOODS (ACROSS 42 SELECTED COUNTRIES) COULD LEAD TO ...[26]	
1.1 million cases of noncommunicable diseases avoided per year	13.2 billion (USD PPP) saved every year due to reduced healthcare expenditure
1.4 million additional full-time workers per year	0.5 increase in GDP

Men are more likely to be obese and so it is no coincidence that men are twice as likely to have a heart attack as women and die earlier from heart disease (at 61 years compared to 71 years for a woman). It is noticeable that Type 2 diabetes among men aged 35 to 54 years (another potential indication of weight gain) is more than twice as likely compared to women, according to Diabetes UK.[27]

Middle Age

It is those people in the middle-ages of life (meaning between the end of early adulthood and the start of retirement, generally between the ages of 45 and 65 years) that are currently experiencing a health crisis because of unhealthy lifestyles.

It is attributed to sedentary lives spent in desk jobs, fast food and the daily stresses that we all encounter. It is the sign of the modern life as we grab fast food between the tasks that seem to overwhelm us.

It does not help that there is extra stress for this is the sandwich generation who are looking after their children while caring for their ageing relatives, so leaving little time to look after themselves.

They can be clearly identifiable by pale complexions, lines across the forehead and bags under their eyes. An additional feature may be the beginnings of accumulated fat around the waist, lovingly described as a 'beer belly' or 'spare tyre', which will only lead to the road to the doctor's surgery for a diagnosis of one or more of the conditions for which obesity and excess weight is responsible.

A study[28] has shown that weight for most of us will fluctuate with the changes in health, environment and other factors throughout life. However, for people in middle age, it is imperative that weight is kept off. For every 11 lbs (5 kg) weight gain before the age of 55 years, there was a 30 per cent increased risk of developing Type 2 diabetes, a 14 per cent increased risk of high blood pressure and an 8 per cent higher risk of cardiovascular disease. In addition, the increased weight during this period was associated with several obesity-related cancers (including breast, bowel, kidney, pancreatic, ovarian and prostate cancers).

It has dire consequences for society in general and for the church in particular. When we are looking for leaders, will we find them incapacitated due to obesity-related conditions? There is the problem of finding capable and willing members of the younger generation, without it being further complicated by factors arising from the sins of overeating and not looking after our bodies. When we are expecting our leaders to live by example, it means in all aspects of life, including living a healthy lifestyle.

Dying early

Being obese can increase the risk of dying early by 50 percent compared to those people who are eating healthily, and the former group are more likely to develop ten out of twelve health conditions including stroke, heart failure or irregular heartbeat, angina, sleep apnoea and chronic kidney disease.[29]

It is important to recognise our weaknesses and also those of people around us so, when you are organising or contributing to a communal meal (e.g. at the church), it is imperative to encourage people attending to eat healthily with modest portions (as well as looking out for all the allergies and intolerances that might be contained in the dishes).

It is ironic that our lifespans in the modern age have increased due to medical advances and better nutrition, but we have stored up numerous problems because of the unhealthy lifestyles that we engage in. It has been calculated that, although we are living longer, the rate of disability has remained the same, so the effect is that our longevity comes with increased periods of disability, largely caused by choices that we made earlier in life.

The clinical advisor to Public Health England's campaign for healthier living, Professor Muir Gray, stated: 'By taking action in mid-life ... you can reduce your risk not only of Type 2 diabetes,

HUGE HEALTH RISKS OF HIGH BMI[30]				
How many times more likely you are to suffer from these conditions if you're overweight				
	Overweight (BMI 25–29)	Class I obese (BMI 30–34.9)	Class II obese (BMI 35–39.9)	Class III obese (BMI 40–45)
Type 2 Diabetes	2.4	5.2	8.8	12
Sleep apnoea	2.4	5.8	12	22
Heart failure	1.2	1.7	2.5	3.7
High blood pressure	1.5	2.2	2.9	3.6
High Cholesterol	1.5	2.0	2.6	3.1
Irregular heartbeat	1.1	1.4	1.9	2.6
Osteoarthritis	1.34	1.67	1.98	2.32
Chronic kidney disease	1.28	1.6	1.87	2.22
Asthma	1.28	1.53	1.73	1.84
Angina	1.15	1.33	1.42	1.57
Stroke or transient ischaemic attack (mini-stroke)	No increased risk	1.08	1.15	1.27
Chance of early death from all causes	0.8 (20% less likely)	0.9 (10% less likely)	1.1 (10% more likely)	1.5 (50% more likely)
HOW TO CALCULATE YOUR BMI				
To find out your Body Mass Index, divide your weight in kilograms by height in metres. Divide the result by your height in metres again.	Less than 18.5		Underweight	
	Between 18.5–24.9		Normal	
	Between 25.0–29.9		Overweight	
	Between 30.0–34.9		Class I obese	
	Between 35.0–40.0		Class II obese	
	Over 40		Class III severely obese	

which is a preventable condition, but you can reduce your risk of dementia and disability, and being a burden to your family.'[31]

Work and obesity

It has been estimated that chronic conditions such as obesity (but also including diabetes and cancer) were costing the United Kingdom economy £21.6 billion every year in lost productivity. The economies of other nations are also being adversely affected in the same way.

The statistics showed that:[32]

- Workers with normal weight, and with no disease burden, report less than 4 unhealthy days per year due to poor health.
- Obese or overweight workers, with a burden of three or more diseases, report 60 unhealthy days per year and over 18 workdays off due to sickness per year.

A study in Spain also showed that obese and overweight employees take more sick days than other colleagues. Members of staff who are too heavy but classed as 'metabolically healthy' are 37 per cent more likely to take time off, which increases to 71 per cent if the employee is 'metabolically unhealthy' (i.e. meeting the three criteria from a list which included having an extended waist and high blood pressure).[33]

In another study by the Centre for Economics and Business Research, it was found that employees' bad health was costing businesses in the United Kingdom nearly £3 billion a year and there could be significant savings if employers were active in helping members of staff to change their lifestyles. These changes included the reduction in obesity (which, in turn, would lead to a lower risk of cancer, heart disease and other chronic illnesses).

In response to this report, Paul McArdle, a dietician who runs a nutrition clinic for BUPA, commented that there are simple things companies can do to encourage employee activity. Examples included starting an after-work running club, encouraging staff to raise money for charity by doing a sponsored 5K walk, or taking advantage of the cycle-to-work scheme (the UK Government's tax-free bikes initiative, which is available to companies with as few as two employees). The size of the workforce is irrelevant as it should not be a barrier to healthy-living initiatives.

He continued: 'Just three in ten employees take a lunch break, and the impact this is having could well be significant as almost half feel their productivity levels plummet in the afternoon around 3 p.m. and as a result lose almost 40 minutes of their day due to this dip. Instead of taking a break to refuel, workers are using props including chocolates, sweets and caffeinated drinks to get them through the day. Taking an entire hour for lunch can often be difficult and is often not necessarily the best way to keep productivity levels up. Best practice for employees is to take breaks at regular intervals throughout the day to help stay alert and keep focused.'[34]

At work, it is easy to submit to the pressure of paperwork and to neglect our wellbeing. It is doing a disservice to our employer if we are not looking after ourselves as he/she will not be getting the best out of us. I have observed a number of times that Christians do not go to the Christian Union or the equivalent as they are too busy, whereas a refocusing of their bodies and minds in activities, such as walking down a flight of stairs, will equip them mentally and physically for the rest of the day.

We are commanded to work for our employers '... with all your heart, as working for the Lord, not for men' (Colossians 3:23). We cannot be obeying this commandment if we are suffering from the complications arising from obesity.

Risks increase

Obese people are statistically at a higher risk of colon, breast, endometrial and gall bladder cancers, sleep apnoea, and gallstones.[35] These conditions will inevitably lead to long-term impairment and even early morbidity.

The increase in breast cancer is caused by oestrogen active fat. The consequence of a woman losing the fat that was produced by oestrogen will be that her hormonal levels will decrease by between 10 and 26 percent. If a woman includes exercise as part of her weight management, the risk will be reduced radically.

It has been discovered that healthy, overweight people and healthy, regular-sized people had the same risk of such conditions as high blood pressure, high blood sugar levels, high cholesterol levels and excess abdominal fat. However, overweight people had slightly higher metabolic markers (e.g. readings of slightly higher blood pressure), which indicated that there was an increased risk of complications later in life.[36]

There is a dual effect of being obese or overweight as the condition can increase both bad cholesterol (LDL) and triglycerides and lower good cholesterol (HDL). Just losing 5 to 10 per cent of your body weight can lead to a noticeable reduction in both LDL levels and triglycerides. As the weight loss increases, it will probably lead to even better cholesterol levels. There is no medication or meditation to increase your HDL, the cholesterol that help lower the LDL. However, it has been discovered that exercising for 30 to 60 minutes a day will increase its elevation by approximately 4 points compared to those people who were not physically active.[37]

The payoff was that, even among non-smokers, people who were the recommended weight increased their longevity when compared to people who were mildly overweight.

Harder to lose weight

It is hard enough to lose weight at the best of times but, for obese and overweight people, it is made far more difficult as the problem is exacerbated by scarred and inflamed fat cells which remain in the body because they are starved of oxygen and will lead to obesity-complicated conditions, such as fatty liver disease and cardiovascular disease.

Being overweight or obese means that there are fewer brakes on the overeating as the lateral hypothalamic area (LHA), the area of the brain that regulates our food intake, is weakened so that we have little control over what and how much goes into our mouths.[38]

There is a natural decline in lung function as we all get older but it will accelerate in people who experience moderate or high weight gain during mid-life. However, the good news is that weight loss puts the brakes on the decline and that people who maintained a healthy weight throughout their adulthood had a less noticeable decline in respiratory health.

The trigger is on

In the normal course of events, the body converts the white fat, which stores energy, into the brown fat, which is used in the expenditure of energy. Fat is stored in special cells, called adipocytes, which are capable of being changed from brown to white. This enables the body either to store the fat (i.e. the white fat) or expend energy (i.e. through the brown fat).

When someone eats, insulin is produced. This insulin then sends out instructions to the body to make brown fat (where energy is to be used).

When someone is not eating or is fasting, the fat is to turn white (to be stored) by the same instructions.

It has been ascertained that, in obese people, the mechanism is defective so that it remains in the 'on' position, resulting in no energy being used and fat continuing to be stored so resulting in weight gain.

Diabetes

Type 2 diabetes is a scourge because it is not only bad in itself with the life-limiting prospect; but increases the risk of developing Parkinson's disease by 31 per cent, particularly if the diabetes is diagnosed in early life. It is easy to overlook the consequences of this life-limiting condition by just concentrating on the diabetes alone.

In turn, those people who had complications arising out of their diabetes had a 49 per cent increased risk of developing Parkinson's disease than those without diabetes.[39]

When people eat about 78 per cent more calories than they

should, their sensitivity to insulin (which turns sugar into energy) decreases dramatically—up to 28 per cent. The problem is that, if this continues on a long-term basis, it could develop into diabetes as the insulin no longer functions and blood sugars remain high.[40]

It could be that you consider yourself to have a body that is only slightly overweight, but there is still a chance that you could have diabetes so it is important to seek medical advice.

Men are 20 per cent more likely to develop Type 2 diabetes than women, which could affect their lives with the high risk of earlier death. There is a correlation with the fact that men are more likely to be overweight than women, which in itself could lead to diabetes.

People with diabetes, especially men, are more likely to experience foot ulcers. Men were also more at risk of diabetic retinopathy (affecting the eyesight) and twice as likely to have a major amputation as a result of diabetes than women. There was a 40 per cent greater risk of men dying of diabetes mellitus as an underlying cause of death than for women.[41]

The knock-on effect on both men and women is that diabetes has a catastrophic effect on the brain leaving the person being two to three times more likely to develop dementia—which most people are unaware of.[42] The majority of people do not consider that the results of obesity and being overweight do, in themselves, have further consequences.

The good news is that Type 2 diabetes can be monitored by medication but, if it is mild enough, it can be managed by changes in the diet.

Dementia

Overweight middle-aged people have an increased risk of dementia. People who are diagnosed with dementia generally had a higher Body Mass Index (BMI) in midlife but a lower one in old age. It is one of the reasons (as we saw earlier) that people in the middle years of life should be aware of their BMI score, being careful as to what they eat and to participate in exercise.[43]

The risk of hypertension is increased if a person is overweight or obese. Even having a slightly raised blood pressure in mid-life may increase the risk of dementia up to 45 per cent, especially if the reading was more than 130/80 mmHG. At present, approximately a tenth of the British population have readings that exceed 140/90 mmHG and are taking prescribed medicines to control it.

It appears that the risk primarily arises when people are diagnosed with hypertension in their 50s, as opposed to their 60s and 70s, as they would have lived with the condition for longer.

Hypertension can lead to mini strokes, damage to the white matter in the brain and a restricted blood flow to the brain (so depriving the organ of oxygen). These are contributors to dementia especially of the vascular form.

Depression

Although it was suspected that depression was connected to obesity, more recent research has made that connection clearer. Dietary fats make their way up the bloodstream and enter the brain in the hypothalamus section. They then accumulate and affect the neurological signals related to depression and other mental health issues.

Although it is often thought that fat-dense foods are comforting and mood-boosting, they do in fact have the reverse effect on our psychological wellbeing in the long term. It is a vicious descending circle because, if you are feeling low, you might treat yourself to more fatty foods (such as chocolate or chips) to make yourself feel better, which would then actually consolidate negative feelings. On my part, I tried to boost myself in the past by eating chocolate and peanut bars with the illogical reasoning that the nuts would negate any effects of the sugary brown substance.

While there is a general awareness that a reduction in fatty food intake can lead to many health benefits (such as better body image, healthy skin and more inclination to exercise), many people do not realise that it also promotes a happier disposition.

When we reach out for that bar of chocolate or other confectionary of choice, we may be giving ourselves a food version of a comfort blanket for a short time, but it is only short-term. The longer lasting effects will be more detrimental to us as our signalling in the brain will be adversely affected.

In order to have the real possibility of good mental health in the future, it is important to have a healthy lifestyle in the present.

Antidepressant medicines

Our bodies create amino acids, such as tryptophan, which increases as we absorb more calories. It was this phenomenon that was investigated as to the impact of a wide range of antidepressants.

In most instances, it was found that weight class, or BMI, negatively affected the efficiency of those antidepressants. It could be that these medicines were in competition with the extra tryptophan that was already in the body.[44] There is a register of conditions that result in extended use of antidepressants leading to withdrawal effects that last for over a year, and obesity is included in that list.[45]

It is worrying because, firstly, depression and other chemical imbalances could be the causation of the obesity.

Secondly, it is observed that weight gain can be a side effect of the antidepressants[46], with the implication that the efficiency of the medicines could be less as they are used on a longer-term basis.

If you are on antidepressant medicines and want to lose weight, it is advisable to talk with your medical practitioner as to the best way forward.

Strokes

The younger age group experiencing strokes was attributed to the likes of diabetes and obesity, together with other outcomes of an unhealthy lifestyle.[47]

FIRST-TIME STROKES ARE HAPPENING EARLIER IN LIFE IN ENGLAND Percentage by age group		
	2007	2016
40−69 years-old	15.3%	20%
Over 70s	64%	59%
Source: Public Health England		

Cancer

Obesity is associated with health conditions that can contribute to the risk of cancer. For example, diabetes, gallstones, inflammatory bowel disease, and poor diet can all increase the probability of cancer. It is estimated that there is a 12 per cent increase of having cancer if a person is overweight. The risk was increased for cancers that were identified as being obesity-related (e.g. kidney cancer and pancreatic cancer), as well as blood and neurological cancers.[48]

The reason why obesity is associated with developing cancer is that there is a very fast increase in the number of cells to cope with the larger body in addition to the secretion of high levels of proteins and hormones which are pro-inflammatory (like oestrogen). It is the combination of these factors that increases the risk of having cancer.[49]

In addition, it has been ascertained that carrying fat around the waistline could be a good indicator of a person's cancer risk. Research has shown that waist circumference and waist to hip ratio could predict similar obesity-related cancer risks in older adults.

It was predicted that an extra 11 cm (4.5 inches) on the waistline increased the risk of obesity-related cancers by 13 per cent. Excess body fat can change the levels of sex hormones, e.g. oestrogen and testosterone, which can cause the levels of insulin to rise and lead to inflammation, all of which are factors in the increased risk of cancer.[50]

Being overweight or obese is the single most preventable cause of cancer after smoking and is associated with thirteen types of cancer, including pancreatic, bowel and breast.

Indeed, overweight and obese people are more likely to have the following cancers: breast cancer (after the menopause), bowel, womb, oesophageal, kidney, liver, stomach, gallbladder, ovarian, thyroid, myeloma and meningioma.

The tragedy is that most cancers caused by obesity can be avoided. The scientists have determined that 40 per cent of all cancers could be obliterated if people change their lifestyle choices. Although smoking is still the most common cause of this condition, the use of tobacco is reckoned to be on the decline; whilst the other causes, notably excess weight, drinking alcohol and consuming less fibre, are on the increase. The problem with obesity is that it could overtake smoking in the near future as the primary cause.

It has been noted that obesity-related cancers are increasing among successively younger age groups. The most noticeable increase is in adults in the 25 to 49 age group, despite the fact that cancer is perceived as predominantly a symptom of old age. The rates of the obesity-related cancers increased greatly among the younger adults, including six types where the rate exceeded that in the older generations (for example, bowel, pancreatic, kidney). By contrast, the non-obesity-related cancers either remained stable or diminished.

Similarly, there were also higher rises among the younger adults compared to the older age groups in relation to womb cancer, gallbladder disease and multiple myloma.

The worrying issue about this list is that it contains two of the most common (breast and bowel cancers) and three of the hardest to treat (pancreatic, oesophageal and gallbladder cancers).[51]

The evidence suggests that the tide of reversing the cancer rates could be slowing or going back to the previous higher rates. In the future, obesity could reverse the progress that has been made to reduce the rate, unless there are any dramatic interventions.

The sobering fact is that, in some cancers, the manifestation of excess body weight during younger adulthood could be a greater influence than weight gain during later life. The increase has been attributed to poor dietary habits such as eating little fruit, vegetables, whole grains, fish and shellfish at the same time as eating too much salt, fast food, and sugary drinks.[52]

There is also proof that sedentary activities such as binge-watching television for more than four hours a day could increase the risk of a man developing bowel cancer, the third most commonly diagnosed cancer for men. In comparison to men who watched one hour or less daily, the risk was increased by 35 per cent for those who watched more. It was not the result of the actual technology, but of the culture of watching the screen. When you are lazily sitting in an armchair, reaching over for your favourite snacks, it is easy to increase all the risk markers for obesity in one session as you will probably not be eating the healthiest of foods and your activity will be limited. Doing something more productive (such as prayer walking or prayer cycling around your neighbourhood) would be better for you, both physically and spiritually.

Although a person may not be in the habit of watching television, they may remain seated without movement while reading or undertaking a hobby. It is important to build in regular intervals for movement (such as getting up from the seated position every hour) in order to mitigate these risks even more.

Strain on ligaments and joints

As we have seen with the effects demonstrated by the MRI scans, obesity also has devastating effects on the ligaments and joints. For every pound (0.45 kg) of weight that is gained, an extra four pounds (1.8 kg) of pressure is placed on each of the knee joints. For example, if there is five pounds (2.26 kg) gained, there is another twenty pounds (9 kg) of pressure on each knee.[53]

As most people walk between 5,000 and 10,000 steps each day, the heavier a person becomes results in more pressure and wearing out of the knee joints.

It does not happen in isolation as the weight gain also puts pressure on the connective tissues around the joints, such as the tendons which connect the muscles to bones. The extra weight placed upon the tendons can cause them to be inflamed and result in tendinitis. Tendonitis may cause redness and pain around the joint, which can be nearly disabling.

In addition, the bursa (a fluid sack near to the joint that assists in keeping the tissues from rubbing against the bones) can be irritated resulting in bursitis. It will result in the same redness, swelling and pain as tendonitis.

If the damage is so bad that it is irreparable, the only option will be to have replacement surgery. If someone is obese, they are twenty times more likely to need the surgery at seven or eight years earlier than someone of a healthy weight. The replacement operation in itself carries its own risks as the anaesthetic process that puts them to sleep can cause strain on the heart that is already weakened by the amount of fat around it.

On top of that, people who are obese are more likely to injure themselves with more complications as the injury heals. An example is that obese people are more at risk of knee joint dislocations (where the thigh bone is separated from the lower leg bones), even undertaking simple tasks like walking down the stairs, where the balance is disturbed by the distribution of fat in the body causing strain on the tendons and muscles as the weight bears down on them. Likewise, fractures of the ankle, hip, thigh and shin bones are more commonly experienced by obese people in cases such as falling.

It is not only adults who are affected as chronic pain, especially in the feet and knees, is evidenced more in children with obesity than by children of healthy weight. An oversized child will also feel the strain on their developing musculoskeletal system—the effects of which will continue to impact their lives into adulthood. The aches and pains that they will feel as they reach maturity would have their beginnings in their infancy and childhood.

In summary, people who are overweight or obese are twice as likely to have pain in the ligaments and joints than those of normal weight.[54]

Hearing loss

Intriguingly, a healthy diet may reduce the risk of acquired hearing loss. It has been assumed that loss of hearing is an inevitable consequence of the ageing process, but it has been ascertained that people who eat food recommended in the healthy eating plans had a reduced risk of decline in hearing sensitivity.

In the mid-frequency range, there was a decline in the risk of a reduction in hearing capability for nearly 30 per cent of women who ate healthily. In the higher frequencies, the risk factor was 25 per cent lower for women who followed the healthy eating recommendations.[55]

Fertility

There are many factors involved in a decreasing population (such as medical reasons, choice and environmental causes) and there are enough obstacles that might be encountered by a couple wanting a child, but the area of obesity and being overweight is one that is controllable.

Being obese can affect adversely the man's sperm and so make it increasingly more difficult for couples to conceive.

Men who are overweight are 11 per cent more likely to have a low sperm count and 30 per cent are more likely to have no sperm in their ejaculation compared to men who were considered to be of a healthy weight.

Obese men were 42 per cent more likely to have a low sperm count compared to those men who were of a healthy weight and 81 per cent more likely to produce no sperm.[56]

It has been assessed that the sperm of an obese man has been irrevocably damaged by the time that they reach the age of 18 years, due to the culture of fast food and ready meals. It has been shown that a poor diet while the male is growing up could reduce his chances of fathering children for the rest of his life. It could be that the diet is deprived of antioxidants putting the sperm under 'oxidative stress,' which would cause their premature demise. The conclusion is that if a couple want a child, they have to live healthy lifestyles from an early age.[57]

The good news is that the situation can be rectified by men eating approximately two handfuls of mixed almonds, hazelnuts and walnuts daily for fourteen weeks, which is calculated to improve their sperm count by 14 per cent and increase the number of viable 'swimmers' by 4 per cent. The reason is that nuts contain omega-3 fatty acids, antioxidants, the vitamin B folate and other nutrients that would improve a man's fertility.[58]

There is also a salutary reminder to women who are wanting to become pregnant. Their lifestyle choices belie that (together with smoking) many women are unprepared to conceive as they drink too much alcohol, are obese or overweight, and eat insufficient amounts of fruit and vegetables. The advice is that women should think about their lifestyle, not just about the folic acid in their breakfast cereal, many years before they think about having a baby.

For women aged between 26 and 30 years who were planning to have children, it was discovered that 96 per cent had iron and foliate deficiencies below the recommended levels in those who were pregnant. In addition, none of the group had the recommended one microgram of vitamin B12, which is essential for the development of the unborn child's nervous system. It would have been preferable for them to have taken supplements before they conceived or, better still, consumed them in fortified or naturally occurring food.

There is a knock-on effect as these deficiencies may have a genetic, cellular, metabolic and/or physiological impact on the developing unborn child. In turn, it will cause that child to experience ongoing consequences through childhood and into adulthood, including the lifelong risk of a continuing susceptibility to diseases.[59]

An example is that children born to mothers with a larger waistline were at a 65 per cent risk of developing autism. The comparison was between those pregnant women whose waist measured more than 31.5 inches (80 centimetres) and those whose waist was less than that size.[60]

Obese mothers also expose their unborn offspring to a 3.5 times higher risk of developing Type 2 diabetes in comparison to a baby born to a woman of normal weight. The significant increase in Type 1 or Type 2 diabetes in their children was 26 per cent for overweight mothers and 83 per cent for obese mothers. It adds to the statistic of four in five children born to obese and overweight mothers being diagnosed with Type 2 diabetes.[61]

Obesity and relationships

It is true that once we have a partner (be it boyfriend, girlfriend, husband or wife), we take less care of our appearance, including what we eat. Although being married is good for your life, particularly regarding mortality and heart attacks (especially for men), it can be devastating for the waistline. It is common for men in particular to show that they are enjoying their wife's cooking maybe a little too much—I know that I did!

In general, it has been calculated that people in relationships tip the scales more heavily than those who are still single. When I look back to the early days of our marriage especially, I shudder at the unhealthy choices that we made, such as the calorie-full shopping that we did (thinking of the quiches and the large quantities of ice cream that we consumed). It did not mean that I was obese but it clearly meant that I became very overweight—the scales told the story that I still put on the weight that was not good for my body.

The paradox is that people in relationships were more likely to make better lifestyle choices, such as drinking less alcohol, smoking less, eating less fast food, and consuming more fruit and vegetables than single people. However, couples tended to weigh more, even if they undertook equitable amounts of physical activity and watched the same hours of television as single people.

The reason for the weight gain could be that because they are settled in a married relationship, they feel as though they do not have to make the same effort to keep their looks. Married people may feel as though they can take their feet off the pedal and be inclined to cease or reduce the amount of exercise that they were doing while they were single and increase their meal portions. It could be that there are many pressures in married life (e.g. time to see more family members gained by tying the knot or, possibly, the young additions to the family) that make the inclusion of exercise more difficult. There are many examples of couples (and, again, it is noticeably the men) who gain inches around the waistline and slip into unhealthy habits.

Catherine Hankey, a health professor at Glasgow University, acknowledged that there were many factors involved and stated: 'I think that the obvious explanations are that you are no longer single and that perhaps may make keeping weight off less important.'[62]

All is not lost, as couples can work together to encourage healthy lifestyles, such as searching for the reduced- or no-calorie foods while shopping and participating in physical exercise as a joint venture instead of slouching in front of the television (especially watching box sets) and munching weight-gaining fast foods.

Vitamin D deficiency

What is often overlooked is not only what does happen to people who carry excess weight, but also what does not happen. Fat around the liver is associated with reduced levels of vitamin D (normally obtained through exposure to sunshine) in men, although not in women.[63]

The reduction in vitamin D increases the risk of developing conditions such as arthritis, asthma and type 1 diabetes due to the decrease in its anti-inflammatory and immune-strengthening benefits. The vitamin also aids in the regulation of blood flow and the prevention of blood clots. It is also beneficial as it repairs and prevents damage to the heart caused by diabetes and high blood pressure.

If men allow themselves to become obese or overweight, not only do they cause harm to their bodies, but they are also obstructing their natural repair system from functioning.

Eating alone

Men who eat alone more than twice a day have a 45 per cent greater risk of developing obesity. In addition, eating alone can result in high blood pressure and high cholesterol as the men were 64 per cent more likely to develop metabolic syndrome (a combination of diabetes, high blood pressure and obesity) which causes them to be at a higher risk of coronary heart disease and stroke.[64]

Women who ate alone were 29 per cent more likely to develop metabolic syndrome.

Those who ate alone were most likely to be single, live alone and miss meals. The point is that households are getting smaller with more people living alone. In a society where marriages break down, single people are delaying getting married for the first time until their 30s and 40s, and more younger people are wanting to live alone, we are seeing that eating alone is a common experience for many.

Eating fast

It is no surprise that, in the age of TV dinners and to-go snacks/lunches, the luxurious pleasure of savouring a meal has become a relic of a past era certainly in many parts of the UK and USA; although generally in Mediterranean countries (such as France, Italy and Spain), the eating experience is still one to be enjoyed. However, it has been discovered that there are health benefits to eating more slowly.

Only 2.3 per cent of the slow eaters developed metabolic syndrome, compared with 6.5 per cent of the medium speed eaters and 11.6 per cent of the fast eaters.[65]

In other words, the fast eaters were five times more likely to develop metabolic syndrome, with the increased risk of heart attack, diabetes and stroke. The fast eaters were also more likely to put on three stone (9 kg) in weight.

The process of eating quickly prevents the brain from noticing that too many calories have been consumed. When the body has taken too many calories on board, it stores them as fat, putting pressure on the heart. The fast-eating causes spikes in the sugar level as well, stopping the insulin from working effectively.[66] It also produces heartburn as the body attempts to absorb all that has been consumed in such a short time, which is only good news for the creators and suppliers of antacids.

It is a very important lesson that we are to take time to eat, rather than eating a hurried meal or grabbing a to-go snack. We are to savour what we put in our mouths, rather than the food in our mouths becoming a meaningless amalgamation of tastes—to chew and take note of the textures. We are to revert back to the days of our ancestors when they knew how to enjoy their meals to the fullest, appreciating the goodness of God on the plate.

Reversing obesity

The good news is that obesity and being overweight is reversable.

Scientists have looked at ways in which the decline in obesity and its accompanying non-communicable (NCDs) (i.e. cancer, cardiovascular disease, chronic respiratory disease and diabetes) could meet the United Nation's sustainable development goals to reduce deaths from those causes by a third by the year 2030.

Nils Lund, a co-author of the report and an associate professor at Memorial University of Newfoundland, Canada, commented: 'If we could just cap obesity at the rate it is today, that would reduce premature mortality by a third. This shows the extent obesity affects chronic disease mortality.'[67]

If we reverse obesity, we can make differences to people's lifestyle and the environment that they live. Ironically, it could increase the money in our wallets as we will be able to work and not be adversely impacted by its effects. We will also know that we are assisting in the fight against climate change and also against inequality for the powerless people in the world.

ACTION POINTS

- *Consider what is a reasonable clothes size for you without being overweight or anorexic. What can you do to get to that clothes size?*

- *Think about the physical and social implications of you being a recommended size.*
- *Be more calorie aware.*
- *Make healthy choices for festive and other special occasions.*
- *How can we practice hospitality to help others eat healthily?*

NOTES

1   See Ahmad Jayedi et al, 'Central Fatness and risk of all-cause mortality: systemic review and dose-response meta-analysis of 72 prospective cohort studies', *British Medical Journal*, 2020, 370: m3324 https://www.bmj.com/content/370/bmj.m3324

2   OECD Health Policy Studies, *The Heavy Burden of Obesity—The Economics of Prevention* (OECD Publishing, 2019)

3   See Ahmad Jayedi et al, 'Central Fatness and risk of all-cause mortality: systemic review and dose-response meta-analysis of 72 prospective cohort studies', British Medical Journal, 2020, 370: m3324 https://www.bmj.com/content/370/bmj.m3324

4   Cancer Epidemiology Unit, Nuffield Department of Population Health, 'Men with larger waists more likely to die of prostate cancer', 1 September 2020, https://www.ceu.ox.ac.uk/news/men-with-larger-waists-more-likely-to-die-of-prostate-cancer

5   Carolyn Thomas, 'What your body fat really looks like', https://myheartsisters.org/2011/12/07/what-your-body-fat-really-looks-like/

6   'Attitudes to obesity: Findings from the 2015 British Attitudes Survey', NatCen Social Research /Public Health England https://www.bsa.natcen.ac.uk/media/39132/attitudes-to-obesity.pdf

7   Cathy Newman, 'Why are we so fat?' *National Geographical*, https://www.nationalgeographic.com/science/health-and-human-body/human-body/fat-costs/

8   NHS Digital statistics cited in 'Obesity-related hospital admissions double in four years', *BBC News*, 4 April 2018, http://www.bbc.co.uk/news/health-43640575

9   Min Gao et al, 'Associations between body-mass index and Covid-19 severity in 6.9 million people in England: a prospective, community-based, cohort study', *The Lancet—Diabetes and Endocrinology 9* (6): 350–359

10 Quoted in Tom Pilgrim, 'Obesity associated with 'higher odds' of Covid-19 hospital admissions – study,' *Press Association*, 11 August 2020, https://uk.news.yahoo.com/obesity-associated-higher-odds-covid-2019346389.html?guccounter=1

11 Source: OECD Health Policy Studies, *The Heavy Burden of Obesity—the Economics of Prevention* (OECD Publishing, 2019)

12 Line Jee Hartmann Rasmussen et al, 'Association of Neurocognitive and Physical Function with Gait Speed in Midlife,' *JAMA Network Open*, 11 October 2019, 2 (10): e1913123

13 OECD Health Policy Studies, *The Heavy Burden of Obesity—The Economics of Prevention* (OECD Publishing, 2019)

14 NHS Digital, *Health Survey for England 2017*, 4 December 2018, https://files.digital.nhs.uk/5B/B1297D/HSE%20report%20summary.pdf

15 Michael Pear, *To Train Up a Child: Turning the hearts of the fathers to the children* (Pleasantville, Tennessee: No Greater Joy Ministries, 1994), https://www.goodreads.com/work/quotes/661339-to-train-up-a-child (I have inserted words in brackets)

16 Jonas Zierer et al, 'The fecal metabolism as a functional readout of the gut microbiome,' *Nature Genetics*, 2018, pp. 790–795, https://www.nature.com/articles/s41588-018-0135-7

17 British Heart Foundation, 'New statistics reveal nations overindulgence over Christmas', 15 December 2015, https://www.bhf.org.uk/news-from-the-bhf/news-archive/2016/december/new-statistics-reveal-nations-level-of-inactivity-and-overindulgence-over-christmas

18 J Birch et al, *A Weighty Issue—A Study of UK Adults' Consumption Behaviours, Knowledge of Calorie and Added Sugar Guidelines and Physical Activity Levels* (Cancer Research UK, March 2017) http://www.

cancerresearchuk.org/sites/default/files/a_weighty_issue_full_report.pdf

19 Laura Donnelly, 'Britain's booming restaurant culture fuels record childhood obesity levels', *Daily Telegraph*, 7 January 2017, http://www. telegraph.co.uk/news/2017/01/07/britains-booming-restaurant-culture-fuels-record-childhood-obesity/

20 Ibid.

21 Richard Wilkinson and Kate Pickett, *The Spirit Level: Why equality is better for everybody* (London: Penguin, 2009), p. 101

22 Kate Lally, 'Brits being 'put on a diet' as fast food chains being ordered to 'calorie cap' meals', *The Daily Mirror*, 19 January 2018 https://www.mirror. co.uk/news/uk-news/brits-being-put-diet-fast-11875690

23 The NHS Information Centre, *Health Survey 2008 (2009)* http://digital.nhs. uk/catalogue/PUB00430

24 The United States figures can be found at: 'Obesity is common, serious, and costly', Centres for Disease Control and Prevention, https://www.cdc. gov/obesity/data/adult.html; 'Overweight & Obesity Statistics', National Institute of Diabetes and Digestive and Kidney Diseases, https://www. niddk.nih.gov/health-information/health-statistics/overweight-obesity

25 *OECD Health at a Glance 2017: OECD Indicators—How does the United Kingdom compare?* 2017, http://www.oecd.org/unitedkingdom/Health-at-a-Glance-2017-Key-Findings-UNITED-KINGDOM.pdf

26 OECD Health Policy Studies, *The Heavy Burden of Obesity—The Economics of Prevention* (OECD Publishing, 2019)

27 'Hazardous Waist? Tackling the epidemic of excess weight in men', *Men's Public Health*, 2005 https://www.menshealthforum.org.uk/sites/default/ files/pdf/hazardouswaist.pdf

28 Y Zenget et al, 'Associations of Weight Gain from Early to Middle Adulthood with Major Outcomes Later in Life', *Journal of the American Medical Association*, 2017, 318 (3): 255–269 https://jamanetwork.com/ journals/jama/fullarticle/2643761?resultClick=3

29 Victoria Allen, 'Proof obesity kills: Study of 2.8 m Britons shows it can raise the risk of an early death by 50%—and being slightly overweight is also deadly', *Daily Mail*, 29 April 2019

30 Ibid.

31 '"Middle age health crisis' warning', *BBC News*, 26 December 2017 http://
www.bbc.co.uk/news/health-38402655; '83% of middle aged adults
living unhealthy lives, say experts', *Daily Mail*, 28 December 2016 http://
www.dailymail.co.uk/wires/pa/article-4069990/Most-middle-aged-
adults-living-unhealthy-lives-say-experts.html

32 Dan Witters and Cynthia English, '"Unhealthy UK Workers"' Lost
Productivity Cost: 21 Billion Dollars', *Gallup News*, 29 September 2011
http://news.gallup.com/poll/149747/unhealthy-workers-lost-
productivity-cost-billions-pounds.aspx

33 Rob Waugh,'Most sick days for overweight staff', *The Metro*, 10 April 2017

34 Paul McArdle quoted in: '"Unhealthy workers" costing employers billions
of pounds every year', *Personnel Today*, 25 May 2011 https://www.
personneltoday.com/hr/unhealthy-workers-costing-employers-billions-
every-year/

35 National Heart, Lung and Blood Institute (NHLBI), 'Overweight and
Obesity' https://www.nhlbi.nih.gov/health-topics/overweight-and-
obesity#Risk-Factors

36 See, for example, 'Are Metabolically Healthy Overweight and Obesity
Benign Conditions?: A Systematic Review and Meta-analysis', *Annals of
Internal Medicine*, 3 December 2013 https://annals.org/aim/
article-abstract/metabolically-healthy-overweight-obesity-benign-
conditions-systematic-review-meta-analysis

37 Georgina E Crichton and Ala'a Alkerwi, 'Physical activity, sedentary
behaviour and lipid levels in the Observation of Cardiovascular Risk
Factors in Luxembourg Study', *Lipids in Health and Disease*, 2015, issue 14,
p. 87 https://www.ncbi.nlm.nih.gov/pmc/articles/PMC4530482/

38 Mark A Rossi et al, 'Obesity remodels activity and transcriptional
status of a lateral hypothalamic brake on feeding', *Science*
28 June 2019, 364 (6447), 1271–1274 https://science.sciencemag.org/
content/364/6447/1271

39 Eduardo De Pablo-Fernandez et al, 'Association between diabetes and
subsequent Parkinson disease: A record-linkage cohort study', *Neurology*,
13 June 2018, http://n.neurology.org/content/early/2018/06/13/

WNL.0000000000005771

40 Catriona Harvey-Jenner, 'The impact binge eating has on your body', *Cosmopolitan,* 12 September 2017 http://www.cosmopolitan.com/uk/body/diet-nutrition/a12226855/impact-body-one-day-binge-eating-insulin/

41 Ibid.

42 Saoirse McGarrigle, 'Many unaware that diabetes tied to higher risk of dementia', *Irish Mirror,* 14 November 2017 https://www.irishmirror.ie/news/irish-news/health-news/diabetes-dementia-risk-disease-brain-11515448

43 See, for example, Archana Singh-Manoux et al, 'Obesity trajectories and risk of dementia: 28 years of follow-up in the Whitehall II study', *Alzheimer's and Dementia Journal,* February 2018, 14 (2), 178–186 http://www.alzheimersanddementia.com/article/S1552-5260(17)33689-0/fulltext

44 Svetlana Puzhko et al, 'Excess body weight as a predictor of response to treatment with antidepressants in patients with depressive disorder', *Journal Of Affective Disorders,* 15 April 2020, vol. 267, pp. 153–170 https://www.sciencedirect.com/science/article/abs/pii/S0165032719325297?via%3Dihub

45 Fiammetta Cosci and Guy Chouinard, 'Acute and Persistent Withdrawal Syndromes Following Discontinuation of Psychotropic Medications', *Psychotherapy and Psychosomatics,* 2020, 89 (5): 283–306 https://pubmed.ncbi.nlm.nih.gov/32259826/

46 Alan Carter, 'Everything you need to know about antidepressants that cause weight gain', *Healthline,* 18 April 2018 https://www.healthline.com/health/antidepressants-that-cause-weight-gain

47 Reported in 'Average age of first stroke in England falls, figures show', *BBC News,* 1 February 2018, http://www.bbc.co.uk/news/health-42871861

48 S B Gribsholt et al, 'Hospital-diagnosed overweight and obesity related to cancer risk: a 40-year Danish cohort study', *Journal of Internal Medicine,* 7 January 2020, 287 (4) https://onlinelibrary.wiley.com/doi/10.1111/joim.13013

49 Cited in Mary Kekatos, 'Being overweight or obese increases the risk of getting ANY kind of cancer by 12 per cent, study finds', *Daily Mail*, 8 January 2019, https://www.dailymail.co.uk/health/article-7862451/Being-overweight-obese-increases-risk-getting-kind-cancer-12-percent.html

50 Ibid.

51 Heinz Freisling et al, 'Comparison of general obesity and measures of body fat distribution in older adults in relation to cancer risk: meta-analysis of individual participant data of seven prospective cohorts in Europe', *British Journal of Cancer*, 23 May 2017, issue 116, pp. 1486–1497 https://www.nature.com/articles/bjc2017106

52 Laura Donnelly, '"Shocking" rise in obesity-related cancers among young adults', *Daily Telegraph*, 4 February 2019, https://www.telegraph.co.uk/news/2019/02/04/shocking-rise-obesity-related-cancers-among-young-adults/

53 Carolyn Thomas, 'What your body fat really looks like', https://myheartsisters.org/2011/12/07/what-your-body-fat-really-looks-like/

54 Frank B Kelley, 'What your weight means for your bones', *Obesity Action* http://www.obesityaction.org/wp-content/uploads/What_Your_Weight_Means_for_Your_Bones.pdf

55 Sharon G Curham et al, 'Prospective Study of Dietary Patterns and Hearing Threshold Elevation', *American Journal of Epidemiology*, March 2020, 189 (3): 204–214

56 G A Ramaraju et al, 'Association between obesity and sperm quality', *Andologia*, 19 September 2017 http://onlinelibrary.wiley.com/doi/10.1111/and.12888/full

57 Henry Bodkin, 'Men's fertility damaged by age of 18 thanks to Western junk food diet, study finds', *Daily Telegraph*, 24 June 2019,

58 Reported in Alex Therrien, 'Sperm quality improved by adding nuts to diet, study says,' *BBC News*, 4 July 2018, https://www.bbc.co.uk/news/health-44695602

59 Mary Barker et al, 'Intervention strategies to improve nutrition and health behaviours before conception.' *The Lancet*, 16 April 2018, http://www.

thelancet.com/journals/lancet/article/PIIS0140-6736(18)30313-1/fulltext

60 Reported in 'Study finds association between mother's larger waist size, child's autism risk', *The Endocrine Society*, 19 March 2018, https://medicalxpress.com/news/2018-03-association-mother-larger-waist-size.html

61 Sarah Young, 'Babies born to obese mothers more likely to develop type 2 diabetes, study suggests' *The Independent,* 20 June 2019, https://www.independent.co.uk/life-style/diabetes-type-2-obesity-mothers-pregnancy-child-study-health-a8966696.html

62 Quoted in 'People in Relationships Gain Weight Because They Don't Care about Their Looks', *Newsweek*, 20 March 2018, http://www.newsweek.com/couples-gain-weight-eating-together-weight-loss-854216; http://journals.plos.org/plosone/article?id=10.1371/journal.pone.0192584

63 Tim Newman, 'Belly fat linked to vitamin D deficiency', *Medical News Today*, 21 May 2018. https://www.medicalnewstoday.com/articles/321851.php

64 A Rom Kwon et al, 'Eating alone and metabolic syndrome: A population-based Korean National Health and Nutritional Examination Survey 2013–2014', *Obesity Research and Clinical Practice*, 20 October 2017 https://www.sciencedirect.com/science/article/pii/51871403x17300960

65 Ibid.

66 Sarah Knapton, 'Gobbling down food increases risk of obesity, heart attack and stroke, study suggests', *Daily Telegraph*, 13 November 2017 http://www.telegraph.co.uk/science/2017/11/13/gobbling-food-increase-risk-obesity-heart-attack-stroke-study/

67 Cited by Sarah Boseley, 'Cutting obesity would slash number of early deaths, research finds', *The Guardian*, 1 May 2019, https://www.theguardian.com/society/2019/may/01/cutting-obesity-would-slash-number-of-early-deaths-research-finds

3 Children

Train a child in the way he [or she] should go, and when he [or she] is
old he [or she] will not turn from it (Proverbs 22:6).

Obesity in the younger generation

As we have observed previously, unhealthy eating and a lack
of exercise is an unhelpful mindset and behaviour that we
can pass onto the next generation. It has to be acknowledged
that many adults do all that they can to guide children wisely, but
still have overweight children who snack in secret.

It has been stated that: 'This is a particularly worrying trend as
obesity in children tracks into adulthood with all its associated
risks. It has been predicted that this is the first generation who are
likely to die before their parents, due to the effects of obesity-
induced cardiovascular disease.[1] It is alarming as the only other
example of a younger generation dying in such numbers before the
previous generation was as a result of the fatalities in World War
One. We are in a war of a different kind with assaults on the
waistlines of our children and young people.

It has been estimated that 10 per cent of children born today will
live to reach their 100th birthday—however, it looks as though they
will be isolated as a large number of their contemporaries would
have succumbed to obesity-related deaths at an earlier age.

Statistics showed that 40 per cent of those aged between 16 and
24 years are overweight or obese, together with 52 per cent of young

adults aged between 25 and 34 years. It means that the generation growing up now will be the fattest since records were commenced.[2]

To place the situation into context, Professor Jaap Seidell of the Free University, Amsterdam, has stated: 'People think [being] overweight is an abnormal response to a normal environment. That's not true at all. It's a normal response to an abnormal environment.'[3]

It is an indictment of our age that we regard obese and overweight children as normal when we are reducing their life expectancy. We do not have the right to do this, yet we encourage the situation by allowing them to eat food full of saturated fats, sugars and excess salt, and encourage them to live sedentary lifestyles.

Country	Males	Females
RATES OF OVERWEIGHT AND OBESITY IN **5–19-YEAR-OLDS** AROUND THE WORLD[4] BY SELECTED COUNTRY		
	% Obese	% Obese
United Kingdom:		
England	30.9	27.2
Northern Ireland	27.67	25.29
Scotland	32.0	28.0
Wales	26.3	26.3
USA	34.5	38.0
Australia	26.1	23.6
China	25.9	17.2
India	4.9	4.7
Brazil	25.8	25.2
Mexico	33.5	39.2
Chile	39.8	44.0
Fiji	24.9	32.1
South Africa	16.2	23.6

The effects of childhood obesity

It has been stated that children who are obese or overweight can experience the following:[5]

- Have increased risk of Type 2 diabetes, high blood pressure, cardiovascular disease and bowel cancer (more on some of these later in the chapter).
- Have a negative impact on their educational attainment.
- Have a low self-esteem and negative body image, and also be limited in how much they partake in physical activity.
- Have increased medical visits.

The effects on children are not only experienced in their schooldays, but many of them take forward these impacts on their lives into adulthood. We have often scarred people before they have even reached working or university age because of the adverse consequences of them being obese or overweight.

As far as the psychological effects are concerned (such as poor self-image), it may very well involve counsellors and other cognitive specialists to help get the person's life back on track. In a way, it is the most difficult of the consequences, even though the physical aspects (such as Type 2 diabetes) will limit their capacity to live life as fully as possible and may even end in their premature death. The effects are preventable, and proper eating and physical activity will help with all aspects of a child's life.

It is not as though children are unaware that they should be eating healthily. For example, it has been shown that children were capable of linking being overweight to eating unhealthily (being able to differentiate between healthy and unhealthy food) and not exercising. An interesting observation was that children who were classified as being obese or overweight were no different in their judgement of a healthy body size than those who were not classified as being overweight.[6]

Although many children do know how to choose and eat healthy foods, many children in the United Kingdom were still buying takeaway food for their lunch at least once a week in 2018. Sixty per cent of 11- to 16-year-olds purchased food such as chips or fried chicken from takeaway outlets at lunchtime or after school at least once a week.

It was also revealed that 48 per cent of primary school pupils and 39 per cent of secondary school students consumed three or more snacks a day.

The most popular snack was fruit amongst the majority of primary and secondary children. However, this choice was closely pursued by less healthier options with crisps (46 per cent) and chocolate (46 per cent) as the snack of choice.

Many children do not like eating healthily, despite knowing what they should consume. In honest responses, 36 per cent of children did not like healthy foods, 20 per cent thought that healthy foods were boring and 12 per cent admitted that they did not know what the healthiest options were.[7] Although the Mediterranean diet is considered to be of the healthiest in the world (being high in fresh vegetables, fruit, whole grains, olive oil and fish), the children in Italy, Greece, Cyprus and Spain are now the most overweight in the continent. The culprits for the increase in weight among Mediterranean children were determined to be junk food and inactivity.

In a lesson to us all, the World Health Organisation (WHO) found that children in Sweden were more likely to follow the Mediterranean diet than those in the south of the continent.

Regardless of what children did or did not eat, the most worrying aspect is that the majority of parents of obese children thought that their offspring were either slightly overweight or normal when challenged about the situation.[8] It illustrates that we can be blind to the effects of unhealthy lifestyles on our own children.

Junk food

There is proof that a junk-food diet (that is high in fat and sugar but low in other nutrients) may have a negative impact on a child's physical, mental and educational development. For example, it was ascertained that a child aged 4½ years who was eating a high junk-food diet was more likely to be in the top 33 per cent on the 'strengths and difficulties hyperactivity sub-scales', based on the Strengths and Difficulties Questionnaire (SDQ), at the age of 7 years.[9]

The impact from national bodies is that Public Health England (PHE) issued guidance in January 2017 that parents were to give children '100 calorie snacks, two a day max' to encourage healthier snacking. The examples of healthier snacks included malt loaf; lower sugar fromage frais; and drinks with no added sugar. Other suitable alternatives were fresh or tinned fruit salad; chopped vegetables and lower fat hummus; plain rice cakes; crackers; lower fat cheese; small low-fat, lower sugar yoghurt; sugar-free jelly; crumpets; and Scotch pancakes.[10]

The recommendation was found to be necessary because the diet of many children was found to contain three times the sugar content than was recommended. In the average year, it could constitute nearly 400 biscuits, more than 120 cakes, 100 sweets, 70 chocolate bars and 70 ice creams, which were consumed with more than 150 juice drink pouches and cans of fizzy drink. The impact can be seen in that each ice cream contains roughly 170 calories, a pack of crisps approximately 190 calories, the average chocolate bar is about 200 calories and a pasty is in the 270-calorie mark. It was maintained that it was not promoting the idea of calorie counting (which could cause the opposite problem of eating conditions such as anorexia and bulimia), but that parents and children were to think more carefully as to what constituted as a healthy snack.

It is recommended that children have, as a daily maximum intake, no more than five cubes of sugar for 4- to 6-year-olds and no more than six cubes for 7- to 10-year-olds.

Children growing into adults

There are knock-on effects for obese children as they enter adulthood since they are more at risk of being obese adults with disabilities and experiencing premature death (with the risk factor ranging from 40 to 70 per cent). In addition, while they are still children, they are also at risk of breathing difficulties, increased risk of fractures, osteoarthritis, cancer, hypertension, stroke, early markers of cardiovascular disease, insulin resistance and psychological effects, which they will take with them as they get older.[11]

Children who are obese are three times more likely to develop oesophageal and stomach cancer, which have a lower survival rate than other cancers associated with obesity (such as bowel, breast and liver). It is estimated that about 5,600 people are diagnosed with either of these two cancers every year.[12]

In addition, morbidity and early mortality in adulthood, arising from childhood obesity and excess weight, can result in disproportionate social marginalization and stigmatization in various areas. It comes with numerous instances of humiliation, from hiding their true body shape to accommodation being made for their size (such as booking two airplane seats).

Socio-economic Impact

It is a complicated relationship with socio-economic conditions. The data for children in early years indicates that there is a strong correlation between overweight/obesity prevalence and economic deprivation, being greater for those living in the most deprived areas.

The reason why there is a higher likelihood that overweight and obese children came from the poorest families was that they were most likely to have obese or overweight mothers themselves, who did not breast feed or breastfed for the shortest duration thus feeding their children solid foods at the earliest opportunity and possibly smoked during the pregnancy.[13]

The children from poor families were then exposed to the following:[14]

- More time watching television and using a personal computer (PC) with all the implications which are discussed later on (including more time watching advertisements for unhealthy food and drinks)
- Later and more irregular bed times

- Less physical activity
- Less active play with a parent
- Live in an area without a playground or other communal activity facility
- Skip breakfast
- Eat less fruit and vegetables.

On a sociological level, children in low- and middle-income countries are vulnerable to low nutrition at the time when they need it most. They will be exposed to high fat, high sugar, high salt, energy dense and micronutrient-poor foods, which will be cheaper to buy but poor in nutrient quality. The consumption of these foods, together with the reduced physical activity, will not address the undernutrition that these children will experience.[15]

It is good that children on low incomes are guaranteed nutritional meals during term times in the United Kingdom, although there are problems during school holidays when the meals are no longer available—an issue that has been highlighted by the footballer, Marcus Rashford. It is for the policymakers to decide what to do specifically on this issue; but, as the Church, we must take it to heart that children in particular from low-income families are not deprived of nutritious food. It could be that there are food drops for families that we are aware of, or we could give generously to organisations like foodbanks who can distribute such food.

Diabetes

The increasing number of children and teenagers being referred for treatment of Type 2 diabetes has caused great concern among the medical community—so much so that it is being termed a 'time bomb.' It was indicated that more than 250 children and young people below the age of 25 years in the United Kingdom had been diagnosed with the condition that is common in adults and is often linked to lifestyle factors such as being overweight. More alarmingly, the condition was also found in children under the age of 5 years old.

Stroke

Young people are placing themselves at a higher risk of an early stroke through being obese or overweight. There is the warning that unhealthy lifestyles and poor diets, together with stress (such as issues relating to school), meant that more young people were being diagnosed with high blood pressure (hypertension), which puts extra strain on the heart and blood vessels. As this strain progresses, the risk of a heart attack or stroke increases.

As the number of strokes has increased amongst people of working age (that is 25- to 64-year-olds), the implication is that the risk factors have increased because of unhealthy practices earlier on in life.[16]

Depression

Among teenagers who were eating a healthy diet for three weeks, it was noticed that their depressive symptoms improved. If the practice of eating healthily continued for three months, there was a continued improvement in their outlook on life.

It meant that the teenagers had to cut back on refined carbohydrates, sugar, fatty or processed meats, and soft drinks. These highly processed foods have been clearly shown to increase inflammation, which is a high-risk factor for depression.

The diet that they ate included the following foodstuffs every day: five servings of vegetables, two or three portions of fruit, three servings of grains, three servings of proteins (such as lean meat, poultry, eggs, tofu or fish), three servings of unsweetened diary, *dairy* three tablespoons of nuts and seeds, two tablespoons of olive oil, and one teaspoon of turmeric and cinnamon.

Turmeric and cinnamon have anti-inflammatory properties, as do nutrient-dense foods like fruit, vegetables, whole grains and fish.[17]

In another study, it was observed that 32 per cent of participants who followed the healthy diet were no longer considered as being clinically depressed after three months. In comparison, only 8 per cent of the group that continued their unhealthy diet and received additional support therapy were in the same position.[18]

We have been given good things to eat by our Creator and yet some of us continue to feed our young people, children and ourselves in an unhealthy way. It is detrimental to their mental as well as physical wellbeing, and will impact them in the long term.

The future

Professor Neena Modi, the President of the Royal College of Paediatrics and Child Health (RCPCH), has commented: 'The science exists for all to see; invest in the health of children and make a big difference to their health in later life and hence to their economic productivity.

'For example, four-fifths of obese children will remain obese as adults and this will result in them losing between 10 to 20 years of healthy life. That's a very frightening statistic and something that the Government should get to grips with.' [19]

The RCPCH has ascertained that this disparity is caused by the advertisement of unhealthy foods on television before the watershed (i.e. 9 p.m. in the UK).

The worrying aspect is that childhood obesity has been linked with a 14 per cent increased risk of living with multiple sclerosis (MS) in adulthood in the United States and 10 per cent in the United Kingdom. MS is an auto-immune disease of the central nervous system, which affects one in 500 people. The risk increases especially if the person smokes.[20]

There is evidence that that overweight children are the objects of bullying and stigmatization from many sources. This will have a negative impact on their futures as their self-esteem and educational attainments (which may be coupled with absenteeism) will be affected, so reducing prospective job opportunities (especially as productivity may be reduced) and overall wellbeing.[21]

It is with these childhood experiences that patterns are set for the child's future life. The mind may be set towards poor emotional and psychological health (such as depression and higher risk of self-harm), low self-esteem, and a damaged relationship with food.[22] In addition, it may result in a higher risk of alcohol consumption and smoking in childhood that have their own healthcare implications, both in the present and also into adulthood.[23]

Fitness

Children who have good fitness levels during their childhood and adolescence are more likely to have better lung function when they reach adulthood; indeed, they are less at risk of developing lung disease. It is important as Chronic Obstructive Pulmonary Disease (COPD) affects approximately 1.2 million people in the United

Kingdom (which is an estimated 2 per cent of the population), so it is the second most common lung disease after asthma.

However, it has been increasing at the rate of 27 per cent over the previous ten years and with an ageing population that will exacerbate the problem. It is an issue that can be dealt with in the present by increasing the fitness levels of the children and young people.[24]

Obese children were 30 per cent more likely to develop asthma than those of a healthy weight, while being overweight still raised the risk by 17 per cent. Although it had previously been suggested that children who had the lung condition were likely to be overweight or obese because they did not undertake enough exercise, a more recent study showed that the weight problem was more likely to exacerbate the asthma rather than vice versa.

It is increasingly obvious that becoming overweight or obese as a child significantly increases your risk of developing asthma both in childhood and adulthood, which again points to the importance of preventing obesity at an early age.

The reason for this causation could be that excess weight prevents the lungs from expanding properly so children are forced to take shallower breaths, which can aggravate the airways. It can also trigger inflammation in the body which can trigger asthma attacks.[25]

Exercise

Although we will be looking at exercise later on, it is important to put a marker down here and note how important is for those still in their childhood stage.

Physical exercise is one method of aiding weight loss, which can assist with obese conditions experienced in childhood. However, it has been ascertained that only 22 per cent of boys in the UK aged 11 to 15 years completed the recommended amount of daily exercise, which fell to 15 per cent for girls in this age group. Active childhoods can produce immediate benefits—there are many longer-term advantages to this action.[26]

There is proof that many overweight children gain weight before they are inactive rather than the other way around because they reduce their physical activity once they have gained the ounces, pounds and stones (or grams and kilograms).[27] It would suggest that the reduction of calorie input is a major contributor to children increasing their exercising. In order to promote exercise in children, there is the necessary breaking of the vicious circle by reducing the weight which in turn will encourage the child to take part in physical activity.

It is something that leaders and workers in the church need to be aware of if they are involved in children's and young people's ministries.

In addition, it has been ascertained that cardiovascular fitness is a predictor of cognition in middle age. The exercise that had been undertaken during childhood and adolescence is an indicator of how successful a person was to be in their future professional life.

The reason for this cause and effect, as explained by neuroscientists, is that completing physical activity to increase cardiorespiratory fitness in childhood is related directly to structure and function of the brain's development, especially in the regions such as the hippocampus (dealing with memory) and the prefrontal cortex (which does not completely form until a person is in their 20s).

(Incidentally, this is the reason why individuals who exercise in their 60s and 70s have a lower risk of developing Alzheimer's disease because of the increased blood flow and increased synapses—the latter being the motorways of the brain that deliver messages from one part to another.)

Ted Garland, the professor of biology at the University of California, also expressed another advantage of exercising while young: 'There's a strong tendency for childhood exercise to have a positive influence. Those who have grown up doing regular exercise are more motivated to get out there and exercise as adults. This could be linked to the effect of exercise on the brain's reward-feedback loops. We know that exercise increases the levels of neurotransmitters such as dopamine and, to an extent, serotonin, and that has a kick-back effect on motivation which persists for quite a lot of time.'[28]

Another recently discovered side-effect is that bone structures have a 'memory' of early-life exercise before puberty commences, that persists long after the exercise has finished, which gives health benefits even in a relatively sedentary adulthood. The childhood activity will produce differences in bone mass, density and mineral content compared to those people who exercised a little or not at all during early life. Even if exercise ceases during adulthood, the differences will persist for ten years or more, especially if the exercise commenced before puberty.

In addition to making those people less predisposed to bone diseases such as osteoporosis, exercise in childhood also affects how they process food, particularly with high-fat diets. With the changes being resident in the bone marrow, it enables those children to be less susceptible to inflammatory-related diseases such as diabetes and cancer as they grow into adulthood.

The start does not even begin in childhood as scientists have discovered mothers who exercise during pregnancy, and even prior to conception, pass on the benefits to their infants. As she is sharing her circulation with the offspring through the placenta, it is inevitable that the baby will experience the changes in the hormone levels or blood lipid levels—all of which affect the energy storage, oxygen capacity and muscle health of the infant when he or she is born. In turn, in a virtuous circle, this has a positive impact on their child's natural ability to exercise, and also perhaps on their motivation to exercise at a subconscious level. The start in the womb will set up their offspring throughout the rest of their lives.[29]

It illustrates well the words of David, when he spoke of God: 'For you created my inmost being; you knit me together in my mother's womb' (Psalm 139:13). It is evidence that the mother's lifestyle before conception and during pregnancy will have a major impact on the physical activity, as well as the mental consequences that it brings, of her unborn child.

The lure of the screen

In research on children aged between 9 and 10 years, it was ascertained that those children who spent more than three hours a day in front of a screen had high risk factors for diabetes, which included more body fat and insulin resistance.[30]

An American researcher has summarised the situation as follows: 'The more TV children view, the more likely they are to be overweight. Reduction in TV viewing constitutes the single most effective way for children to lose weight.'[31]

In short, less time watching Teletubbies (and Peppa Pig and other popular children's television programmes) will result in smaller telly tummies.

To back up this statement, there was a study in China that found that when the population watched more TV, the chances of them being obese increased; indeed, every hour of watching increased the likelihood.[32]

It is something that needs to be considered seriously as, in England (for example), it was estimated that the average child aged between 5 and 15 years spends approximately 16 hours a week online and a further 13.5 hours watching television. This is more than double the recommended combined screen time and opens them up to more viewing of HFSS (high in fat, sugar and salt) food and drink advertising.[33] It has been suggested by research that the viewing time of children under 4 years old to televisions, computers and smart devices should be limited to 90 minutes a day so that the risk of obesity in later years is reduced.

The situation starts early in a child's life, for it has been estimated that toddlers watch 1 hour of television a day on average, which rises to approximately 7.25 hours when the child is 9 years old. The experts from the European Academy of Paediatrics (EAP) and the European Childhood Obesity Group (ECOP) have expressed the concern that childhood obesity has grown by an 'alarming rate' and that parents should comprehend the health impact of social media and screen use on their children.[34]

It could be because children get less sleep when watching

television in their rooms, snacking in front of their screen, the effect of the blue rays emanating from the screen that disrupts the circadian rhythm. Even the effect of having an electronic device in the room has an effect on sleep patterns. Girls could also be affected by the fact that they are generally less physically active than boys in this age group, so it is the perfect storm when a number of obese factors come together.

The authors of the research put it succinctly: 'While our screens have become flatter, our children have become fatter.'[35]

To assist in this objective, the experts recommend that:[36]

- Children do not have televisions in their bedrooms.
- Televisions should be turned off during advertising breaks.
- Parents should refrain from using iPads, smartphones or televisions as 'babysitting or calming' techniques.

History

There is a propensity for history to repeat itself. A study by researchers from the University of Medina has shown that childhood obesity is more prevalent in families where obesity is part of its history. Where the parents or grandparents experienced high blood pressure, diabetes, high cholesterol or heart disease, the children have a greater risk of being overweight.

Interestingly, it is the younger siblings that are more susceptible than their older ones. There could possibly be a genetic correlation, but there is a greater emphasis on the lifestyle that is perpetuated, such as the consumption of unhealthy food.[37]

The challenge

Jesus talked about people causing children to sin, that it would be better for them to have a large millstone around their neck and to be drowned in the sea (Matthew 18:6). When we introduce them to the lure of unhealthy living and start them on the road to worshipping the idol of gluttony, we are precisely doing that. We are often guilty of putting spare tyres of fat around our children, while putting millstones around our own necks.

The good news is that these trends can be reversed—such as having a healthy BMI through sensible eating and physical exercise.[38]

ACTION POINTS

- *Protect our children and young people in our church from influences that will affect their food choices. Encourage them to be physically active.*
- *Protect our children and young people in our family from influences that will affect their food choices. Encourage them to be physically active.*
- *Instruct them about the lure of the television and tablet screens.*

NOTES

1 *Obesity in the UK*, https://www.birmingham.ac.uk/research/activity/mds/centres/obesity/obesity-uk/index.aspx

2 'Millennials top obesity chart before reaching middle age', *Cancer Research UK*, 26 February 2018, http://www.cancerresearchuk.org/about-us/cancer-news/press-release/2018-02-26-millennials-top-obesity-chart-before-reaching-middle-age

3 Hella Hueck, *Betutteling moet uit hetverdomhoekjel*, 12 September 2017, https://www.rtlnieuws.nl/economie/column/hella-hueck/betutteling-moet-uit-het-verdomhoekje

4   https://data.worldobesity.org/tables/prevalence-of-child-overweight-including-obesity-3/

5   See, for example, Royal College of Paediatrics and Child Health, State of Child Health Report 2017, RCPCH 2017, p. 54

6   Cited in: James Williams et al, *Growing Up in Ireland national longitudinal study of children: development from birth to three years infant cohort, Report 5* (Department of Children and Youth Affairs, Dublin, 2013) http://www.lenus.ie/hse/bitstream/10147/555696/1/DevelopmentFromBirthtoThreeYears.pdf

7   The BNF survey cited in: Helena Horton, 'Majority of schoolchildren buy takeaway for lunch at least once a week, child obesity study', *Daily Telegraph*, 11 June 2018, https://www.telegraph.co.uk/news/2018/06/10/majority-schoolchildren-buy-takeaway-lunch-least-week-child/

8   WHO survey cited in: Lara Keay, 'Mediterranean diet is falling out of favour with southern Europeans: Children in Italy, Greece, Cyprus and Spain are now the fattest on the continent', *Daily Mail*, 29 May 2018, https://www.msn.com/en-gb/health/diet/mediterranean-diet-is-falling-out-of-favour-with-southern-europeans-children-in-italy-greece-cyprus-and-spain-are-now-the-fattest-on-the-continent/ar-AAxIH5t

9   Louise Bazalgette, *For Starters* (Demos, London, 2012), pp. 28–29

10 Amy Packham, '100-Calorie Snack Campaign Sparks Debate About Calorie Counting For Kids', *Huffington Post UK*, 27 January 2018 https://www.msn.com/en-gb/health/diet/100-calorie-snack-campaign-sparks-debate-about-calorie-counting-for-kids/ar-AAvctEB; Sarah Boseley, 'Limit children to two sugary snacks a day

11 Department of Health, *Healthy Lives, Healthy People: A call to action on obesity in England* (Department of Health, UK, 2011), p. 5, https://www.gov.uk/government/uploads/system/uploads/attachment_data/file/213720/dh_130487.pdf ; Public Health England, *Guidance: Childhood obesity: applying All Our Health,* 1 April 2015, https://www.gov.uk/government/publications/childhood-obesity-applying-all-our-health/childhood-obesity-applying-all-our-health

12 Jessica L Petrick et al, 'Body weight trajectories and risk of oesophageal and gastric cardia adenocarcinomas: a pooled analysis of NIH-AARP and

PLCO Studies', *British Journal of Cancer*, 28 March 2017, issue 116, pp. 951–959, https://www.nature.

13 A Goisis, A Sacker and Y Kelly, 'Why are poorer children at high risk of obesity and overweight? A UK Cohort Study', *European Journal of Public Health*, 10 December 2015, http://eprints.lse.ac.uk/64241/1/Goisis_Why_are_poorer_children%201%20.pdf com/articles/bjc201729

14 A Goisis, A Sacker and Y Kelly, 'Why are poorer children at high risk of obesity and overweight? A UK Cohort Study', *European Journal of Public Health*, 10 December 2015, http://eprints.lse.ac.uk/64241/1/Goisis_Why_are_poorer_children%201%20.pdf

15 World Health Organisation, *Obesity and overweight*, updated October 2017 http://www.who.int/mediacentre/factsheets/fs311/en/

16 Natalie Healey, 'Blood pressure warning: more young people at risk of stroke', *Netdoctor*, 20 September 2017 http://uk.pressfrom.com/lifestyle/family-relationships/-207557-blood-pressure-warning-more-young-people-at-risk-of-stroke/

17 Cited in: Sandee LaMotte, 'Healthy diet improves depression in teens, study says', *CNN*, 9 October 2019, https://edition.cnn.com/2019/10/09/health/healthy-diet-improves-depression-wellness/index.html

18 Cited in: Max Lugavere, 'How your next meal could help fight depression and stress', *CNN*, 20 March 2018, https://edition.cnn.com/2018/03/20/health/food-depression-stress/index.html

19 Royal College of Paediatrics and Child Health (RCPCH), 'Fragmented approach to child health damaging long term health of the nation warns Royal College', 7 February 2018 https://www.rcpch.ac.uk/news/fragmented-approach-child-health-damaging-long-term-health-nation-warns-royal-college

20 Julia Pakpoor et al, 'Estimated and projected burden of multiple sclerosis attributable to smoking and childhood and adolescent high body-mass index: a comparative risk assessment', *International Journal of Epidemiology*, 26 August 2020, https://academic.oup.com/ije/advance-article-abstract/doi/10.1093/ije/dyaa151/5897122?redirectedFrom=fulltext

21 R M Puhl and J D Latner, 'Stigma, obesity, and the health of the nation's children', *Psychological Bulletin*, 133 (4), 2007, 557–580, https://www.

researchgate.net/profile/Janet_Latner/publication/6244412_
Stigma_Obesity_and_the_Health_of_the_Nation%27s_Children/
links/00463524153d2c2a40000000/Stigma-Obesity-and-the-Health-of-
the-Nations-Children.pdf

22 Y Kelly, P Patalay, S Montgomery and A Sacker, 'BMI Development and Early
Adolescent Development Psychosocial Well-Being: UK Millennium Cohort
Study', *Paediatrics*, Volume 138, number 6, December 2016, http://pediatrics.
aappublications.org/content/pediatrics/138/6/e20160967.full.pdf

23 Ibid.

24 Robert J Hancox, Finn Rasmussen, 'Does physical fitness enhance lung
function in children and young adults?', *European Respiratory Journal*,
2018: 51 http://erj.ersjournals.com/content/51/2/1701374

25 Cited in Sarah Knapton, 'Obesity may be fuelling the rise of childhood
asthma', *Daily Telegraph*, 25 November 2018, https://www.telegraph.co.uk/
science/2018/11/26/obesity-epidemic-may-fuelling-rise-childhood-
asthma/

26 David Cox, 'Young at heart: why children who exercise become healthier
adults', *The Guardian*, 30 August 2017 https://www.theguardian.com/
lifeandstyle/2017/aug/28/young-at-heart-why-children-who-exercise-
become-healthier-adults

27 B S Metcalf et al, 'Fatness leads to inactivity, but inactivity does not lead
to fatness: a longitudinal study in children', *Archives of Disease in
Childhood*, issue 10, 2011, pp. 942–947

28 Quoted in: David Cox, 'Young at heart: why children who exercise become
healthier adults', *The Guardian*, 30 August 2017 https://www.theguardian.
com/lifeandstyle/2017/aug/28/young-at-heart-why-children-who-
exercise-become-healthier-adults

29 David Cox, 'Young at heart: why children who exercise become healthier
adults', *The Guardian*, 30 August 2017 https://www.theguardian.com/
lifeandstyle/2017/aug/28/young-at-heart-why-children-who-exercise-
become-healthier-adults

30 See, for example, 'Children's screen time linked to diabetes risk factors',
National Health Service, 14 March 2017, https://www.nhs.uk/news/
diabetes/childrens-screen-time-linked-to-diabetes-risk-factors/; Katie

Forster, http://adc.bmj.com/content/archdischild/early/2017/02/06/archdischild-2016-312016.full.pdf

31 Cited in: A Sigman, *Remotely Controlled: How television is damaging our lives and what we can do about it*, (London: Vermilion, 2005), p. 157

32 Ma GS et al, 'Effect of television viewing on pediatric obesity', *Biomedical Environmental Science*, issue 15, pp. 291–7

33 Ofcom, *Online overtakes TV as kids' top pastime*, 16 November 2016, https://www.ofcom.org.uk/about-ofcom/latest/features-and-news/childrens-media-use. The recommended amount of screen time by the Department of Health's Change4Life is no more than two hours of screen-based entertainment a day. (Change4Life, *Top tips for top kids* [Department for Health, 2009, https://campaignresources.phe.gov.uk/resources/campaigns/17/resources/63])

34   Mazur et al, 'Reviewing and addressing the link between mass media and the increase in obesity among European children: The European Academy of Paediatrics (EAP) and the European Childhood Obesity Group (ECOP) consensus statement', *Acta Paediatrica*, 107, (4), April 2018, pp. 568–576 http://onlinelibrary.wiley.com/doi/10.1111/apa.14136/full

35 'TVs in children's bedrooms 'increase risk of obesity'', *BBC News*, 2 June 2017, http://www.bbc.co.uk/news/health-40120286

36 'Children should have time on smartphones and TV limited to 90 minutes to prevent obesity, researchers claim', *Daily Telegraph*, 22 November 2017 https://www.telegraph.co.uk/news/2017/11/22/children-should-have-time-smartphones-tv-limited-90-minutes/

37 Domenico Corica et al, 'Does Family History of Obesity, Cardiovascular, and Metabolic Diseases Influence Onset and Severity of Childhood Obesity?', *Frontiers in Endocrinology*, 2 May 2018, https://www.frontiersin.org/articles/10.3389/fendo.2018.00187/full

38 Marietta Charakida, John E. Deanfield, 'BMI trajectories from childhood: the slippery slope to adult obesity and cardiovascular disease', *European Heart Journal*, 21 June 2018, 39 (24), 2271–2273 https://academic.oup.com/eurheartj/article-abstract/39/24/2271/4985706?redirectedFrom=fulltext

4 The obsession

And I'll say to myself, 'You have plenty of good things laid up for many years. Take life easy; eat, drink and be merry' (Luke 12:19).

It is one of the ironies of life that, when we feel stressed, we head for the unhealthy foods. It can be the mid-morning snack, the afternoon hit about 3 p.m. or the need for comfort food as we work away or sit idly in the evening. The biggest draw is an emotional one, be it depression, boredom or any other reason that we can think of.

It has been stated that emotional eating is one of the hardest cycles to break, hence the proliferation of so many weight-losing organisations. It is a situation that is common, regardless of culture, race or nationality. It also appears to be a common occurrence throughout the world, regardless of experiences.

We can kid ourselves like the rich fool (Luke 12:13–21) that we have time to rectify the misuse of our bodies, especially if we are younger. The Bible warns us that the years may be shorter than we think and that we may even be contributing to the diminishment of time. It is not only true spiritually but it is also a physical reality, as this passage is often used as a reminder that eternal life is but a breath away.

The American Psychological Association (APA) has reported that people tend to look for high-calorie, high-fat foods in those times when they feel stressed, despite the fact that people store more fat when they are stressed than when they are relaxed.[1]

The APA, in their Stress in America TM survey, detailed how people often had undesirable consequences of binge eating, such as feeling sluggish or lazy and feeling bad about their bodies.

In the survey, 38 per cent of the respondents had reportedly overeaten or eaten unhealthy foods in the past month because of stress. Half of these adults (49 per cent) had confessed to engaging in these behaviours on a weekly basis or more often. In addition, 27 per cent of the respondents stated that they eat to manage stress, while 34 per cent of these confessed to it becoming a habit of overeating or eating unhealthy foods because of stress.

In contrast, 30 per cent of the adults missed meals because of stress, with 41 per cent of people doing it on a weekly basis or more often.

The majority of those who skipped meals (67 per cent) did so because of a lack of appetite, with 26 per cent stating that they did not have the time to eat.

After overeating or eating unhealthy meals, half of the respondents (49 per cent) felt disappointed in themselves, 46 per cent felt bad about their bodies, and more than a third (36 per cent) felt sluggish or lazy afterwards. It just increases the guilt feeling, which could feed into a seemingly endless vicious circle where disappointment increases and so a raid to the biscuit tin seems like the solution—with greater frequency and larger or more biscuits (for example).

Among those who skipped meals, 24 per cent felt sluggish or lazy and 22 per cent reported being irritable.[2]

The paradox is that people eat unhealthily because they are depressed and then they are depressed because they have eaten unhealthily, as we have already noted, so the vicious circle is increased in intensity. It is made worse by consuming products that are high in sugar and fat, which affects our weight and also give us a mood booster that is only temporary.

The worrying aspect is that these behaviours we have let become habits are already part of the psyche of our teenagers and will inevitably become that of our children unless we choose to make a difference now.[3]

We need to deal with this sin of gluttony in our lives right now before it seeps into the mindset of children so that they think it is normal. The warning has been given by God that, if we permit this idol to take hold of our lives, it will be perpetuated to our offspring— He will punish 'the children for the sin of the fathers to the third and fourth generation' (Exodus 20:5; Numbers 14:18; Deuteronomy 5:9; Jeremiah 32:18).

We need to stop seeing the resort to food as a solace and solving all the problems that stress brings on. Geneen Roth explains the situation like this: 'There's a sort of desperation: "I have to handle this somehow and food is right there ... And not only that, [food] doesn't talk back; it doesn't get drunk; it doesn't go away; it doesn't abuse; it's always available; and its cheaper than asking for help."'[4]

The problem with this proposed solution is that we always head towards the unhealthy products, seeing it as a type of reward that we deserve for being in the situation. One of these food stuffs is sugar which (as we will note in another chapter) has many negative impacts, including the ability to turn down stress-related hormones, so (for example) making us more susceptible to binge on cakes and sweets. Those stress levels also escalate our cortisol levels so, although our appetites are lessened in the short-term, they are further heightened in the longer term with the consequence that we become increasingly hungry.

The satisfaction of having high-calorie foods does not alleviate the emotions that stress brings; indeed, there may be more stresses caused as we worry about our consequent disappointment in ourselves and resulting body image (another subject that we address later on).

We must learn to deal with the stress through eating nutritious food and with communication with others. Roth reminds us: '[You're] eating from needs that have nothing to do with your body but have much more to do with your mind, with stress, with your feelings—using food in many ways to soothe or comfort or numb what you believe cannot be soothed or comforted or numbed in any other way.'[5]

A typical 'Western diet' which was high in fat, sugar and salt, and low in fibre has been shown to be a factor in a more aggressive development of a strong inflammatory response in diseases such as strokes, heart attacks and diabetes. The cause was the unexpected increase in certain immune cells in the blood, activating many genes inside those progenitor cells that direct the body's immune response. Even after the diet resumed back to normal and the initial state of inflammation had gone, the genes that had been activated remained in an alarm state.[6]

In order to avoid such adverse effects, we need to work out why we crave such a diet. It could be for human connection, space, stimulation, quiet—all the things that can be negotiated with other people rather than trying to obtain it out of a packet. The resulting excessive and/or unhealthy eating could also be a way of keeping God out of our lives—after all, He is fully aware of the situations that we are in.

If food is idolatry insofar as it replaces God in the priority of our lives, then we prevent God from speaking to us in those hard times. Munching loudly through a packet of crisps makes it harder to hear what God is saying to us!

There should be the awareness that food that fills but does not nourish should be cut out of our lives. We are clearly warned: 'When you sit to dine with a ruler, note well what is before you, and put a knife to your throat if you are given to gluttony. Do not crave his delicacies, for that food is deceptive' (Proverbs 23:1–2). It is a radical attitude to think about the food that you about to consume before you put fork to plate or put your hand into the packet.

Indeed, instead of dealing with the issues that confront us, the excessive and/or unhealthy eating will propel us into negative emotions as the survey reveals. It will become a downward spiral of negativity: 'The problem with turning to food to deal with uncomfortable feelings, which so many of us do, is that you still have the uncomfortable feelings and now you have feelings of shame and guilt added on top of those. It's not like it actually makes anything go away. It doubles it.'[7]

The proviso is that we are not to totally deprive ourselves. We are to determine what is truly a reward and what is a crutch to get us through a difficult situation. The work of the Holy Spirit is to live within us (John 14:25–27) and to strengthen us, and He also uses other people when we need someone with skin on. However, there may be more imaginative ways in which we can treat ourselves to a reward than to rely on food.

ACTION POINTS

- *Maintain a healthy eating habit.*
- *Combat cravings by considering healthy alternatives (e.g. raw vegetables, a moderate portion of nuts).*
- *Think through any snacks—are you really hungry or are you depressed? Will it help you in the long or short term? Is the food needed or is it a crutch?*

NOTES

1 P Björntorp, 'Do stress reactions cause abdominal obesity and comorbidities?', *The International Association for the Study of Obesity, Obesity Reviews*, 2001, 2 (2), 73–86

2 American Psychological Association, 'Stress and Eating—Trying to eat our way to stress relief', https://www.apa.org/news/press/releases/stress/2013/eating.aspx

3 American Psychological Association, 'Stress in America TM- Teens Adopting Adults' Stress Habits', 11 February 2014, https://www.apa.org/news/press/releases/stress/2013/stress-report.pdf

4 Geneen Roth quoted in: Gwendolyn Purdom, 'Why you overeat when you're stressed—and how to break the cycle', 3 January 2018, https://www.wellandgood.com/good-food/why-you-stress-eat

5 Ibid.

6 University of Bonn, 'Fast food makes the immune system more aggressive in the long term', 11 January 2018, https://www.uni-bonn.de/news/010-2018

7 Geneen Roth quoted in: Gwendolyn Purdom, 'Why you overeat when you're stressed—and how to break the cycle', 3 January 2018, https://www.wellandgood.com/good-food/why-you-stress-eat

5 Body image

Man looks on the outward appearance, but the LORD looks at the heart (1 Samuel 16:7).

Introduction

The inclusion of a chapter on body image is because many, particularly young, people see the 'perfect body' portrayed on social media, posters or television and yearn to have the same.

One reaction can be that they aspire to be like the image before them, hence the burgeoning number of gym memberships that have been taken out. The alternative is to rebel against society's 'norm' and so become physically larger, or it could be that the person gives up hope altogether that they could possibly aspire to be like the portrayal.

There is the 'comparison obsession' that has pervaded modern society, as observed by Thomas J DeLong, a professor at the Harvard Business School. He has commented: 'More so than ever before ... business executives, Wall Street analysts, lawyers, doctors and other professionals are obsessed with comparing their own achievements against those of others ...This is bad for individuals and bad for companies. When you define success based on external rather than internal criteria, you diminish your satisfaction and commitment.'[1]

It has been stated that, 'Fashion and beauty pages are equally problematic: beautification is equated with "self-improvement" and the conservative, neat and matching fashions suggest that a girl's appearance should "please both boyfriend and boss alike and threaten the authority of neither".'[2]

Technology and appearances

The problem appears to have increased as we have relied increasingly on the technology that can improve our lives, but which also has the power to disrupt and destroy. As one writer commented: 'It is often shocking to see how narrow the physical ideas held up to young women truly are ... While the magazines I read at school were never feminist tracts, they were not littered, as girls' magazines are now, with page after page of expensively dressed and made-up young girls exposing such skinny, airbrushed bodies.'[3]

In a survey undertaken by the YMCA England and Wales, 62 per cent of 15- to 16-year-olds felt that social media raised expectations of their personal appearance. It has been exacerbated by the influence of celebrity culture, which was identified as being the main influence of 58 per cent by those in the 11–16 age group.[4]

Denise Hatton, the chief executive for the YMCA England and Wales, commented: 'We've all been guilty of only posting our most flattering pictures on social media. While there's nothing wrong with wanting to show yourself from your best angle, it's important that we still like ourselves when we're not looking our best, which is probably the majority of the time for most of us.'

She continued: 'Today's beauty standard is completely unobtainable, leading us to constantly feel bad about our bodies and looks. This is particularly the case for young people and it can have a serious effects on their mental and physical wellbeing.

'It's time to take back control of how we feel about our bodies and celebrate our real self so that everyone can feel confident in their body this summer and beyond.'

Psychological Impact

Obesity and being overweight are more than physical manifestations, as they also have implications for our psychological wellbeing.

Evidence shows that mental health problems have increased exponentially among girls in the previous decade as their use of social media has exploded. The unrealistic images are in collision with the ever-increasing reliance on unhealthy food and reduced physical activity. The casualty in this conflict is the mental state of people today, particularly the younger generation,

One of those who are concerned, Dr Bernadka Dubicka, the chair of the child and adolescent faculty at the Royal College of Psychiatrists, has observed that there is a growing crisis in children and young people's mental health and, in particular, an impending storm in mental distress and depression among girls and young women.

She commented that social media, such as Snapchat and Instagram, '... can be damaging and even destructive' to the mental wellbeing of girls. There's a pressure for young people to be involved 24/7 and keep up with their peer group or they will be left out and socially excluded.'

There have been numerous news headlines demonstrating the

fact that fat-shaming goes on, particularly (but not exclusively) among young teenage girls and promoting the idea that the recipients of the messages should be immeasurably thin, almost harking back to the whale-bone corset days of the Victorian era.

This situation is backed up by the numerous reports about body image, which has become a major issue in the United Kingdom (and elsewhere), where there seems to be two poles of thought with those who are obese/extremely overweight on one end of the equation and those who are anorexic on the other. We go through the extremes from venerating our bodies to abusing them, with some people oscillating between those two opposite ends of the spectrum on a regular basis.

Beware of the opposite

C S Lewis wrote a masterpiece, The Screwtape Letters, where an older devil (Screwtape) advises a younger one (Wormwood) on how to tempt his human 'patient'. He addresses the issue of 'gluttony of delicacy', where it is not so much about excess but about the delusion of 'watching our weight' whether it goes up or down. Screwtape tells of the 'patient's' mother: 'She is always turning from what has been offered to her to say with a demure little sigh and smile, "Oh, please, please ... all I want is a cup of tea, weak but not too weak, and the teeniest weeniest bit of really crisp toast." You see? Because what she wants is smaller and less costly than what has been set before her, she never recognises as gluttony her determination to get what she wants, however troublesome it may be to others.'[5]

He continued: 'She would be astonished—one day, I hope, will be—to learn that her whole life is enslaved to this kind of sensuality, which is quite concealed from her by the fact that the quantities involved are small.'[6]

Having said that, we should be aware of the condition of orthorexia nervosa, which is the unhealthy obsession towards eating healthily. In the worthy attempt to eat healthily, the person then becomes fixated on what they eat, which can often be excluding essential food groups. Any consumption of unhealthy food, however, usually will result in 'punishments' such as stricter adherence to their diets, excessive fasts and harsher exercise regimes.

The scale

An example of the scale of the problem can be demonstrated in a report[7] in the United Kingdom which has found that:

- 60 per cent of adults felt ashamed of the way that they looked.
- 70 per cent of adult women and 40 per cent of adult men reported that they had felt pressurised by television and magazines to have the perfect body.
- 34 per cent of adolescent boys and 49 per cent of adolescent girls have been on a diet to change their body shape or to lose weight.
- It was estimated that approximately two-thirds of the population suffer from negative body image.
- 42 per cent of girls and young women felt that the most negative part about being a female is the pressure to look attractive.

One third of men would sacrifice a year of their life to achieve their perfect body.

There is a disturbing increasing degree of dissatisfaction with body shape, leading to wider damaging consequences for the whole of society's health and wellbeing, as each individual expressed their dislike of the body that God had given to them. It is not constricted to any particular sector of society, although children and adolescents are the most susceptible.

Among children and adolescents, body image dissatisfaction has led to the undermining of self-confidence, increasing depression, and the onset of a range of physical, emotional and societal problems. They were the least likely to engage in learning and to participate in school activities, with half of all bullying being experienced by those pupils with poor body image.

It is important that adults (such as parents and teachers) should be aware of this factor and so encourage the children and teenagers who are the bullies, or could be, to understand what their peers are going through in order to set up peer support. Conversely, positive body image was conducive to good public health and social environments for the young people.

Media

The media has definitely contributed to this false sense of body image by criticising the body weight, size or appearance of the people featured. The approach has been intensified by the lack of body diversity and an over-reliance on image manipulation.

However, there is the caveat that not all people (especially girls and women) are affected mentally, emotionally and/or physically by their exposure to thin models in publications. This clarification of the situation has been written: 'The media are often blamed for spreading the message that women are thin, and for making women feel bad about themselves. This seems overly simplistic ... ignoring the fact that women voluntarily expose themselves to thin media images, that such exposure can actually be pleasurable, and that most women do not develop eating disorders.'[8]

Another study augmented this conclusion as to why women may not be dissatisfied with their bodies after comparison with media photographs: 'First, a woman may have low body dissatisfaction because her body shape is similar to that of the standard depicted in the media ... A second possibility is that even if a woman is substantially heavier than the media standard, she may possess low body dissatisfaction because body-image images are not important to her, because, for example, she is confident in her skills and abilities in other areas. A female with low body dissatisfaction for either reason would not be likely to be threatened by exposure to media images and increased weight concern would be unlikely.'[9]

Another report has expressed that the effect of media images will adversely affect '... especially those women who are dissatisfied with their body who are likely to suffer negative self-evaluative consequences from exposure to images of physically attractive female individuals.'[10]

It has been discovered that one of the effects of seeing the men 'with abs to die for' and women with slender bodies is that up to one million people in Great Britain use anabolic steroids and other image- and performance-enhancing drugs (IPEDs) to alter the way that they look. It is this image-altering reason, rather than sporting purpose, that many commonly in the 20–24 age group are subjecting their physiques to these dangerous chemicals, although it is in use from 13 years at the youngest to mid-70s at the oldest. The pursuit of the perfect body is not without high risk mentally, emotionally and (ironically) physically.[11]

A further study has agreed that body image is predisposed to a person's perception of their own body (although it refers principally to anorexia and bulimia, it could apply equally to overeating): 'Low self-esteem is a risk factor in disordered eating, with evidence suggesting that the development of bulimic symptoms may be affected both directly by the presence of low-esteem and indirectly by the interaction of low-esteem with other factors. However, eating disorders are usually preceded by chronic dieting and body dissatisfaction, which themselves are related to low self-esteem. And it is also important to note that some women with eating disorders also have other disorders, such as anxiety and depression, that are also related to low self-esteem. In short, there is a complex set of relationships through which self-esteem has its effects on vulnerability to eating disorders. Nonetheless, on the whole, we conclude that low self-esteem is a concurrent and prospective risk factor for eating disorder symptoms.'[12]

Hospital admissions

When considering body image, the consequence on our medical services is not often considered. The impact of the media has far-reaching outcomes whether it is on the public purse (if we live in societies where the hospitals are funded by the state) or on the insurance contributions (where hospitals are privately funded).

The result is often an increase in hospital admissions for eating disorders as we have seen earlier. Another result has been the increase in cosmetic surgery by 20 per cent since 2008. The supposition is that the increase in this statistic has been accelerated by the proliferation of the images in advertisements.

In addition, behaviours that sacrificed health for appearance included steroid abuse, smoking to stop weight gain or becoming exercise dependant, which results in side effects such as muscular-skeletal injury or fatigue.

Moral vacuum

Another casualty in the pursuit for body perfection has been the decline in morals as people seek popularity through cosmetic surgery. It could be in the centrefolds of some dubious publication or the appearance on 'celebrity' reality shows. The pain undergone on the operating table does not always result in the expected delights, with the same character flaws remaining, regardless of what miracles the surgeon has undertaken. A liposuction does not always equal delight with the result, as there may be still psychological issues regarding self-worth that need to be dealt with. As Christine Rosen has observed while giving hope: 'We are not yet a nation of Narcissi, content to stare happily into the pool, our surgically enhanced self-esteem intact but our character irrevocably compromised.'[13]

The effect is also found in family life as wives become uncomfortable about their husbands viewing their bodies. A total of 16 per cent of respondents had not been naked in front of their husbands for the previous twelve months or more. Nearly a half of this quorum stated that it was because they were insecure in their appearance, while a further third blamed a slump in their sex drive. Almost 40 per cent admitted that their relationship had suffered consequently and 36 per cent confided that their constant attempt to cover up had led to rows between the spouses.[14] A significant part of the problem is that their husbands too are subjected to the 'perfect' images projected in the media. A consequence may be that they are dissatisfied with their wives' bodies as they are compared with the billboard and magazine portrayals of what an 'ideal' body should look like. So, body image has an impact not only in the lives of individuals, but also in marriages and families.

A psychologist, Linda Papadopoulos, observed: 'Over the past three decades there has been a dramatic increase in the use of sexualised imagery in advertising. While most of the imagery features women, there has been an increase in the number of sexualised images of children. Sexualised ideals of young, thin, beauty lead to ideals of bodily perfection that are difficult to attain, even for the models, which perpetrates the industry practice of 'airbrushing' photographs. These images can lead people to believe in a reality that does not exist, which can have a particularly detrimental effect on an adolescent.'[15]

Her report then gave the example of how adult clothing is now provided in smaller sizes so that it has become 'normal' for children to wear provocative items. There are the child beauty competitions where the garments are suggestive—and the concept of body image is ingrained on the young minds at an impressionable age. In some countries, there is the provision of beauty pageants for young children—further exposing them to mindsets and attitudes that they are not ready for, as they are exploited by adults for all manner of reasons, such as financial implications and the desire to show off our children as products that we have produced.

From childhood up onto adulthood, we are all exposed to the provocative images, which inevitably lead to physical manifestations. The charity BEAT has brought together statistics from various sources which indicate that 1.6 million people in the UK have an eating disorder, with 1.4 million of them being women (the breakdown includes 10 per cent of these people having anorexia and 40 per cent having bulimia). As a result of the anorexia, there has been an increase in young women having breast implants.

It is not just adolescents that were affected, as eating disorders were developed in children as young as 6 years-old and as old as 70 years-old.[16]

God's solution

God has provided many ways of improving our self-esteem, including one that does not cost any money. It has been ascertained that any person struggling with body confidence issues could benefit by going for a brisk walk. There was a clear indication in the research that walking in natural surroundings, compared with built-up ones, made a radical difference to a person's mental wellbeing and confidence.

Viren Swami, professor of social psychology at Anglia Ruskin University, has commented: There are several reasons why exposure to nature could be having this effect on positive body image. It might be that it distances people, physically and mentally, from appearance-focused situations that are one of the causes of negative body image. It is also possible that exposure to environments with depth and complexity restricts negative appearance-related thoughts. More specifically, natural environments hold your attention—a process known as 'soft fascination'. This is often accompanied by feelings of pleasure, such as when you are drawn to the sight of a setting sun.

He also added that the process of spending more time outdoors may encourage people to appreciate the amazing functionality of their own bodies, so removing the comparison of their own physical appearance with that of others.[17]

However, it is more than the things God has given to us; it is the relationship with God Himself that will make the difference. John Eldredge has written: 'We are made in the image of God; we carry with us the desire for our true life of intimacy and adventure. To say we want less than that is to lie.'[18]

Tony Reinke has helpfully stated: 'Whether or not we see it, worship is the fundamental dynamic of our moulding. And this is why, no matter how fiercely independent we are, we never find our identity within ourselves. We must always look outside of ourselves for identity, to our group and to our loves. Both dynamics reveal the truth: we are becoming like what we see. We are becoming like what we worship. Or, to put this in Facebook terms directly, we are becoming like what we like.'[19]

When Jesus commanded us to 'love your neighbour *as yourself*' (italics added, Matthew 19:19 quoting Leviticus 19:18), He was making a radical statement. He emphasised the importance of how we view ourselves—seeing ourselves through the lens of God— which has social consequences. It will have an impact on us as those who are being bullied and those who bully, and in a host of other situations, when we realise that we think we do not have worth, whereas God has completely different ideas. He loved us so much that He was willing to give up His life so that we would be in relationship with Him (John 3:16).

We are a new creation when we accept the lordship of Jesus Christ, so our minds should be being transformed by the Holy Spirit. We are urged by Paul that, '... in view of God's mercy, to offer your bodies, as living sacrifices, holy and pleasing to God—that is your spiritual act of worship. Do not conform any longer to the pattern of this world, but be transformed by the renewing of your mind. Then you will be able to test and approve what God's will is—his good, pleasing and perfect will' (Romans 12:1–3).

There should be the desire that God would fill us and help us in our thinking. David reminds us of God's determination to correct our thought processes: 'Surely you desire truth in the inner parts, you teach me wisdom in the inmost place' (Psalm 51:6). When we start on the inside with God transforming our lives, the consequence will be a change in how we perceive our bodies.

If we are wanting, really wanting, to allow God to have total control over our lives, and that includes our bodies, we will want Him to fashion our bodies as He wants—not obese or overweight, nor abusing it with a lack of food. He does not want us to go to extremes, but to live in the healthy way for which He created us.

As David Alan Black has commented: 'If your body is a temple where God lives, then it is also a tool that He deserves to use. We are to utilise our bodies to honour and glorify God.'[20]

There is the saying that God does not make rubbish, which is true as you were made for His glory and He wants you to see you as He sees you. When you see yourself from God's perspective, you will want to treat your body in the best possible way.

Our template is to be that of Jesus who came in bodily form –He was born, He ate, He was tired, etc.—so He was like us in all ways except sin. It was interesting that one of the temptations that He faced concerned His image and food, especially as He was hungry after forty days of fasting (Matthew 4:1–4; Luke 4:1–4). He did not sacrifice His mission—what He was about—but He was able to empathise with what we go through without sinning (Hebrews 4:15).

As the Church—God's people—we have the benefit of gathering together to get a right focus on God and so remind ourselves of who we are in Him. It is one of the reasons that we are encouraged to meet together (Hebrews 10:25), especially as we live in an age that demeans the body by consuming unhealthy food.

We need to remind ourselves that the words 'in Christ' and 'in him' were mentioned nine times in Ephesians chapter 1, as prompts that our identity is to be in Christ. It is not in the weight around our waist or the double chins; it is in the assurance that we have been saved by the grace of God.

It is because we have been brought into a new relationship with Jesus, that we know we will have new bodies in heaven, as we come in an amazing congregation to praise God (1 Corinthians 15:44; 1 Corinthians 5:1–5; Revelation 21:5). It does not mean that we are to misuse our mortal frames, but we are to use it as a practice for when we get to heaven—the place where there will be no obesity or excess weight with their consequences.

ACTION POINTS

- *Consider how social media and advertising has an effect on your body image.*
- *See your identity as being in Christ.*

NOTES

1 Thomas J DeLong, 'Why chronic comparing spells career poison?' 20 June 2011, http://fortune.com/2011/06/20/why-chronic-comparing-spells-career-poison/

2 Cited in Joanne Hollows and Angela McRobbie, *Feminism, Femininity and Popular Culture* (Glasgow: Manchester University Press, 2000), p. 168

3 Natasha Walter, *Living Dolls: The Return of Sexism* (UK: Virago Press, 2010), p. 67

4 These statistics and the following quotes by Denise Hatton and Bernadka Dubicka are from Nazia Parveen, 'Social Media and celebrity culture "harming young people"', *The Guardian*, 23 July 2018 https://www.theguardian.com/lifeandstyle/2018/jul/23/social-media-and-celebrity-culture-harming-young-people

5 C S Lewis, *The Screwtape Letters* (London: Harper Collins, 1998), pp. 65–66

6 Ibid., p. 66

7 ll Party Parliamentary Group on Body Image: YMCA, *Reflections on Body Image*, (May 2012) http://ymca-central-assets.s3-eu-west-1.amazonaws.com/s3fs-public/APPG-Reflections-on-body-image.pdf

8 J Polivy and C P Herman, 'Sociocultural idealization of thin body shapes: an introduction to the special issue on body image and eating disorders', *Journal of Social and Clinical Psychology*, 23 (1), February 2004, 1–6, https://www.researchgate.net/publication/240296534_Sociocultural_Idealization_of_Thin_Female_Body_Shapes_An_Introduction_to_the_Special_Issue_on_Body_Image_and_Eating_Disorders

9 Heidi D Posavac, Stephen S Posavac and Emil J Posavac, 'Exposure to media images of female attractiveness and concern with body weight

among young women', *Sex Roles,* issue 38, 1998, pp. 187–201, https://link.springer.com/article/10.1023/A:1018729015490

10 D Trampe, D A Stapel and F W Siero, 'On models and vases: body dissatisfaction and proneness to social comparison effects', *Journal of Personality and Social Psychology,* issue 92, 2007, pp. 106–118

11 Reported in Steven Morris, 'Up to a million Britons use steroids for looks not sport', *The Guardian,* 21 January 2018, https://www.theguardian.com/society/2018/jan/21/up-to-a-million-britons-use-steroids-for-looks-not-sport Complications include: testicular atrophy, change in sex drive, sleep difficulties, aggression, mood swings, acne, injection site pain, depression, hair loss, liver disease, chronic cardiovascular pathologies, and addiction to steroids.

12 P Gaul et al, 'Self-esteem, personality, and eating disorders: Baseline assessment of a prospective population-based cohort', *International Journal of Eating Disorders,* 3 (3), May 2002, 261–273, https://www.researchgate.net/publication/11444197_Self-esteem_personality_and_eating_disorders_Baseline_assessment_of_a_prospective_population-based_cohort

13 Christine Rosen, 'The Democratisation of Beauty', *The New Atlantis,* Number 5, Spring 2004, pp. 19–35, https://www.thenewatlantis.com/publications/the-democratization-of-beauty

14 Amie Keeley, 'Poll reveals one in six women won't let husband see them naked', *Daily Mail,* 26 October 2013, https://www.news.com.au/lifestyle/relationships/poll-reveals-one-in-six-women-wont-let-husband-see-them-naked/news-story/b3dcb99ae82db4006661e50cd5870891

15 Linda Papadopoulos, *Sexualisation of Young People,* February 2010 http://dera.ioe.ac.uk/10738/1/sexualisation-young-people.pdf

16 BEAT, *Beat Eating Disorders: Statistics for Journalists,* https://www.beateatingdisorders.org.uk/media-centre/eating-disorder-statistics

17 Sabrina Barr, 'Spending more time in nature can give you a positive body image, study claims', *The Independent,* 22 January 2018, https://www.independent.co.uk/life-style/health-and-families/nature-body-image-positive-countryside-study-anglia-ruskin-perdana-university-college-london-a8172651.html

18 John Eldredge, *Desire: the journey we must take to find the life God offers*, (Nashville, Tennessee: Thomas Nelson Inc., 2007) p. 165

19 Tony Reinke, *12 Ways Your Phone is Changing You* (Wheaton, Illinois: Crossway, 2017), p. 112

20 David Alan Black, 'Ageing and Finishing Well', 28 December 2018, https://credomag.com/2018/12/aging-and-finishing-well/

6 Sugar

The chief culprit of obesity and being overweight is commonly regarded to be sugar, with the dual impact both on the waistline and on the teeth.

Sugar is a carbohydrate that occurs naturally in food. There are different types including monosaccharides (which includes glucose)—otherwise known as 'simple sugar'. This type is the stuff of life as it is the primary source of energy and the necessity that keeps the brain functioning well along with the other organs of the body.

As the inevitable result of consuming sugars (which are necessary to maintain life), there will always be a variable amount of blood sugar (interchangeably known as 'blood glucose') in the body, as the level will depend on what you have eaten, when you ate and the activity afterwards. The level will be determined by how it is dealt with by insulin, the chemical produced by the pancreas.

There is evidence that, as we consume excess sugar to what we need, our brain's reward systems are activated so we crave not only even more sugar, particularly more harmful processed varieties, but also other substances. It can be classed as a behavioural addiction, where we become hooked onto a behaviour because the action itself gratifies us and so we need increasing amounts to keep up that satisfaction. It has been calculated that our reward systems are altered after a few weeks.

The World Health Organisation (WHO) suggests we are to consume no more than 25 grams of sugar a day, which is the equivalent of two tablespoons or about half a can of coke.[1]

Good news

As we have already seen, there are many types of sugars, although the body cannot readily do much with fructose, which is mainly found in processed foods.

However, it is not all bad as can be seen in the seven carbon sugars found in avocados (for example), which are especially good for you. Other natural sources include ripe fruit, maple syrup and honey.

In the light of the good sugars, it is important that, by reducing or cutting out processed sugar, the other sugars are not excluded. The brain needs a constant source of energy, so initiating insulin to store fat. The key to a healthy brain and the optimal body mass index is to avoid too much insulin production, which is the result of taking in too much processed sugar.

The high nutrient sugars (such as whole fruits, pure fruit juice and dairy products) produce an amino acid called tryptophan, which in turn is the ingredient of serotonin. The latter chemical is the item that helps us feel happy. Tryptophan is also present in the fibre of vegetables like kale, which is made up of sugar that is 'slow burning'.

Although there are many sugars that are essential for us, we still end up consuming an excess amount of those sugars, which have detrimental effects. From now on, when we refer to 'sugar', it will be in regard to the processed type.

The effects of the harmful sugars can be manifested in many ways as we shall see.

Cancer

It has been found that processed sugar 'wakes up' cancer cells and makes the tumours more aggressive.[2] If we cut out processed sugars, it will effectively prevent the tumours from forming.

The impact is that, in our medical facilities, there will be tailor-made diets for cancer patients to cut out or reduce this substance, which will deactivate the cancer-cell multiplication. If we are looking after our bodies, it is another reason to cut out or reduce our intake of processed sugars.

Physical health

The occurrence of too much sugar can be the cause of headaches as there is a sudden sugar rush followed by the consequent drop in blood glucose levels. It is advisable that the sugar intake is reduced if a person is experiencing migraines more than once a month.[3] It is a simple step, by merely taking care of what we consume, that can reduce the pain and also the interruption in our lives.

In addition, it has been found that a diet that is rich in sugars is also the cause of hormonal problems, especially for women. The net result is that the stress levels are increased, as are the effects of the premenstrual syndrome (PMS) and the menopause. The consequences of fatigue, cravings and mood swings are evident as a result.[4] It is debilitating and causes much physical, mental and emotional distress—effects that can be reduced, to various degrees, by minimising or cutting out products containing processed sugars.

There are also the inevitable consequences of having too much sugar if the aim is to lose weight. The body will not use up the fat stores in the liver, muscles or around the waist if it can utilise the energy obtained from sugar.[5] The result will be that increased fat will be stored around the middle as we consume more sugar (an example being the 'beer belly' where sugars from alcoholic drinks are retained in the abdominal area). In addition to a sedentary lifestyle, sugar as part of the regular diet will add on the weight without any effort. Research among Japanese men has discovered that there was 'a significant association between sugar intake and weight gain', even after age, body mass index, total calorific intake, alcohol, smoking and regular physical exercise was taken into consideration.

The literature review came to the conclusion that there was 'consistent evidence that increasing or decreasing intake of dietary sugars from current levels of intake is associated with corresponding changes in body weight in adults.'[6]

In addition to losing weight, we will be slimmer and trimmer as a reduction in sugar will lead to higher levels of testosterone and reduces the levels of oestrogen. The hormone leptin will also be increased so we are more likely to be aware of when we are full. The result will be a decrease in belly fat and an increase in muscle mass.

Mental health

A diet that is rich in starchy and sugary foods can lead to higher levels of inflammation in many parts of the body, including the brain, which is not the case with diets that are mainly consisting of vegetables and healthy proteins. The inflammation of the brain could lead, in turn, to the onset of depression or stress. It could be the cause of why high glycaemic-index foods (that is foods with easily accessible sugars) are connected to an increased risk of depression, especially in women.[7] when stressful occasions occur, it is a natural response to reach out for chocolate or another sugary substitute. However, it is the start of a downward spiral as the more sugar you consume, the more anxious you will become. The explanation is that processed foods strip away and deplete vital nutrients such as the B vitamins, omega 3s, magnesium and other key nutrients that help to prevent mental health issues.[8]

It has been calculated that men who ate more than 67 grams of sugar a day had an increased risk of mood disorders by a fifth compared to those whose intake was less than 39.5 grams (1.39 oz). This outcome could be the result of high sugar and fats in diets reducing the protein BDNF (Brain-derived neurotrophic factor), which influences the growth and development of nerve cells in the brain.

Another reason put forward was that the rapid decline in blood glucose levels after the initial sugar rush could adversely affect the hormonal balance, so upsetting the mood of the person.[9]

On the longer-term repercussions, there has been the discovery by scientists that links sugar consumption with Alzheimer's Disease, as people whose brains were worse at breaking down glucose had more brain plaques (abnormal clusters of protein fragments and build up between nerve cells) and tangles (twisted strands of another protein in dead and dying nerve cells), which are two of the most noticeable signs of the condition.[10]

However, it is not only older people that are affected mentally but also the younger generation. Excess sugar consumption by mothers during pregnancy can impair their child's cognitive abilities and speech functions. In contrast, those mothers who consumed fruits and foods that contained natural fructose improved their child's cognition, which was especially augmented if that child ate fresh fruit regularly.

Dr Rhonda Patrick commented: 'Maternal sugar consumption, particularly from sugar-sweetened beverages, was associated with poorer childhood cognition including non-verbal abilities to solve novel problems, poor verbal memory, poorer fine motor, and poorer visual-spatial/visual motor abilities in childhood.'[11]

The effects can have an impact on all of us as we experience the brain crash and the ensuing brain fog. Evidence is found in difficulty in focusing, finishing tasks in a timely manner (if we finish at all), and reduced energy. It is because a diet high on processed foods, containing large amounts of sugar and salt, may probably be deficient in important minerals, vitamins and antioxidants required to boost energy and give a clear brain.[12]

Ageing

The overuse of sugar can progress to long-term damage to the skin proteins, collagen and elastin, which could result in premature wrinkles and looking older. It could also be a factor in the imbalance of the female menstrual hormones, resulting in acne along the jaw line.

The imbalance of hormones arising from sugary products may lead to acne on the skin in people of all ages, as well as the possibility of increasing eczema in those who are susceptible to the condition. It is because increased levels of insulin lead to high levels of the hormone insulin-like growth factor 1 (IGF-1), which has been linked with severe acne activity.[13]

Constant cravings and low energy

Sugar is addictive and provides a reward mechanism by releasing dopamine, a hormone that is similar to the experience of being addicted to drugs.

Glucose is a vital building block for producing energy throughout the body, so it is important to keep the levels balanced. When sugar is consumed, the hormone insulin is produced by the pancreas to enable the transfer of glucose to the body cells and so the rush of energy is experienced. When the energy has been used up, the body then demands more sugar to replenish the reserves and restart the cycle. Indeed, the greater the sugar input, the greater the consequential energy decline.

In addition, as we have seen, leptin is the hormone that instructs the body that it has consumed enough food. However, there may be resistance developed as a result of consuming too much fructose, although the removal of this substance from the diet will mean that the leptin will act in the normal way.[14] It could be that sugar is the agent that prevents the body from realising that it has had enough. We will look further at the issue in the section on healthy eating

What is worrying is that, as the sugar intake increases, the amount of insulin is produced in greater quantities. The build-up of glucose in the blood will result in symptoms such as fatigue, hunger, brain fog and high blood pressure.[15] Over time, the outcome will be insulin resistance and Type 2 diabetes being diagnosed. A study has stated that, even after factoring in social, economic and dietary factors: 'Duration and degree of sugar exposure correlated significantly with diabetes prevalence ... while declines in sugar exposure correlated with significant subsequent declines in diabetes rates.'[16]

The sugar rush at night will have negative results for our sleeping patterns, especially as our bodies should be settling down in preparation for a restful sleep (see the chapter on sleep).

Liver failure

The sugar surges cause the liver to work excessively, which leads to its stress and inflammation. Fructose causes the development of non-alcoholic fatty liver disease, where the fat accumulates throughout the organ. It will lead to scarring of the liver and will progressively culminate to inflammation, scarring, cirrhosis and even liver failure.[17]

In order to reduce or even eliminate the risk factor, we need to drastically reduce or even dispose of sugar in our diets. We need to give our livers, these delicate organs, a chance!

Unexplained bloating

Harmful bacteria and yeast feast on sugars so the latter is fermented in the colon. The overproduction of gas can proceed to pain after eating, uncomfortable bloating and flatulence.

With all the fast foods that are eaten in excess (as experienced in over 60 per cent of US diets), there is a possibility that digestive problems will occur. Dr Farshad Fani Marvasti, the director of public health, prevention & health promotion at the University of Arizona College of Medicine, explained: 'These foods have various chemicals and additives in them that are very difficult for our bodies to digest and process.'[18] In addition, the additives that often accompany sugary foods and drinks are toxic to our microbiome (that is the good bacteria in our bodies).

Nutrition deficiencies

The use of high sugar diets means that nutrients, such as vitamin D, calcium and potassium, are reduced.

This results in an increased risk of fatigue, osteoporosis and muscle weakness. These effects will add to the problems already being experienced by carrying too much weight.

People, whose diets constituted of 18 per cent or more calories from sugar, had lower levels of the essentials like folate, calcium, iron, and vitamins A and C. As we shall observe when we look at healthy eating, it is important to have a balanced diet—one that will benefit us physically and mentally.

Weakened immune system

The production of undesirable bacteria and yeast as the consequence of a high sugar diet will affect the immune system. It is important as over 70 per cent of our immune system is positioned in the gut.

It is possible that being overweight or obese will result in being more susceptible to diseases and infection because our immune cells are compromised as our gut bacteria is imbalanced with certain bad bacteria and fungi. It puts us at risk of contracting any manner of chronic diseases, including those that affect our autoimmunity.

It is, therefore, important to encourage the good bifidobacteria, which processes vegetable matter.

Kidney disease

There is a link between drinking too much sugary fizzy drinks and kidney disease.

It is because uncontrolled high blood sugar can damage the blood vessels of the kidneys and so destroy their capability of filtering the blood, which in turn allow toxins to build up. As the toxins increase, possible outcomes are obesity and overweightness, together with Type 2 diabetes, which are all high-risk factors for major kidney disease.

Laboratory studies showed that drinking twelve times the WHO's recommended amount will lead to enlarged kidneys and poor kidney function.[19]

Gout

Gout is a type of arthritis that causes sudden, severe joint pain, often lasting for five to seven days before it gets better. The attack is usually in the big toe but it can occur in other joints in the body such as the feet, hands, wrists, elbows or knees. There is also the symptom of hot, swollen, red skin over the affected joint. There might be repeated incidences.

Gout was once considered to be the province of the rich, with the folklore being that it was the result of drinking too much port. However, modern studies have shown that there is more to this condition than that simplistic explanation.

It is caused by the largescale production of purines, which are chemicals that cause the manufacture of uric acid—the source of this painful condition.

In addition to steak, kidneys, livers, seafood and alcohol, sugar is also a high-risk factor for gout as uric acid is also the by-product of sugar metabolism.[20] If a person is already experiencing trouble walking due to carrying weight and osteoporosis as a result of obesity and overweight, the addition of gout will reduce mobility even more.

High blood pressure

It is useful to understand the workings of blood pressure, so it is explained in Appendix B (p. 311).

Although hypertension is normally associated with salty foods, eating many sugary products will also be detrimental to the blood pressure.

The reason is because fructose manufactures uric acid (as we saw with gout), a product that is associated with high blood pressure. The sugar surge will be instrumental in producing more uric acid, which will go unchecked unless it is monitored.[21]

Heart disease

It is well-known that smoking and being sedentary are major risk factors for heart disease; however, the effects of having a diet with excess sugar (such as having diabetes and being overweight) are also risk factors, especially for women.

It has been ascertained that people with high-sugar diets are more susceptible to heart failure than those on diets with high starch or high fat contents. It is important to get our blood pressure levels down to relieve the impact on our hearts.[22]

People who receive 17 to 21 per cent of their daily calories from sugar are 38 per cent more likely to die from heart disease compared to those who limited their calorific intake from sugar to 8 per cent.[23]

Oral health

The activity of bacteria in the mouth is centred on breaking down food particles, which results in acid being produced. If there is not the regular cleaning of the teeth (at least twice a day), flossing and application of mouth wash, together with regular visits to the dentist and hygienist, then the resulting acid will combine with the saliva and produce plaque around the teeth and gums. If the plaque is not removed, tooth decay is an inevitable consequence.

The importance in these preventative measures is that there is a higher risk of tooth deterioration if the diet is high in sugar.[24]

We need to think about the health and appearance of our teeth, as they have a huge role in having a positive body image.

Approximately a quarter of children (24.7 per cent) experience tooth decay by their sixth year. Indeed, tooth decay/extraction is the most common cause of hospital admissions for children aged 5 to 9 years.[25] It has been calculated that a child in England has a tooth removed in hospital every ten minutes due to preventable decay. Public Health England (PHE) have produced statistics that indicate that approximately 141 children (some as young as one year-old) experience a tooth being removed per day. In addition to the difficulties with sleeping and eating, it accounts for 60,000 days missed from school.[26]

As we get older, the situation does not get better as it appears that one in four adults in the UK admitted to not brushing their teeth twice a day—the minimum that we should be aiming at.

Research has been undertaken as to the effect that bacteria-laden plaque has when it is allowed to form on the teeth. It found that, out of approximately a tenth of the participants (7,100 out of 66,000) who developed cancer, those with a history of periodontal disease were more than three times as likely to have oesophageal cancer and twice as likely to have gallbladder cancer compared to the participants with healthy teeth and gums.

In addition, the risk of lung cancer, skin cancer and breast cancer were increased by 31 per cent, 23 per cent and 13 per cent, respectively. Even among non-smokers and non-drinkers, there was a 12 per cent increase in the risk of cancer which indicates that good oral health is paramount.

It has been suggested that pathogens are transported to different parts of the body by the saliva coming down from our mouths to reach other parts of our bodies, so they come into contact with the stomach and oesophagus when we swallow, or with the lungs when we aspirate.[27]

The effects of teeth decay are also the results of our gluttony, so we are affected in more ways than we usually think.

Cutting out sugar

It can be done over a number of stages:

1. Detox: There can be a three-day detox when you eat foods containing less than 15 grams of sugar per serving. It covers not only the obvious sources (e.g. cakes, ice cream, fizzy drinks and alcohol), but also the less obvious (e.g. juices, yoghurts and bread). These foods can be replaced by foods containing healthy fats (e.g. avocados, nuts).[28]

2. Initial pains: There will be the realisation that the process of weaning off sugars will be difficult as the body realises the new normal of not relying on sugars. It could mean getting more irritable and achier—more than usual—as the body adjusts to not having the sugars to fire up the hormones and to having to get the energy from the fat and muscle reserves.

3. Temptation: There will be the temptation to seek sugar substitutes (such as saccharine which equally has adverse

effects on the body), but this must be overcome. The substitutes will fool the body in gaining weight and continue the desire for sweet foods, the very thing that you want to overcome.

4. Positivity: There will be opportunities when you fall from your set goals, but it is important not to beat yourself up. If you go for a sugary food out of forgetfulness or because you are depressed or tired in the moment, you need to forgive yourself and move on, as the overall destination is more important than the dips in the road. Ironically, forgiving yourself may give you that same euphoric feeling that you would have from a sugar rush. It might also be easier if you have a buddy, mentor or any encourager as you embark on the journey to wean yourself off sugary substances, so that you will not feel alone. It is also important not to become preoccupied with eating healthily as it could develop into orthorexia (that is, spending excessive time thinking and worrying about food and eliminating food), which could lead to an eating disorder.

5. Do not be hungry: A good process is to eat three balanced meals with two snacks a day, all without sugars. Alternatively, five smaller meals can be planned. The plates can be filled with fibre-full foods (e.g. fruits, vegetables and whole grains) together with protein which will stave off hunger.

6. Dealing with cravings: It is often the case that thirst is mistaken for hunger. The requirement for energy can be satisfied by non-sugary drinks such as water.

7. Treat yourself: On the odd occasion, such as meals out with friends, there can be the treats with controls in place as to the

portion size. It is to be recognised that these are not to be a common occurrence.

8. Recognise why: The reduction in sugar is so that you can live a healthy lifestyle, with a reduction in the conditions that come with unwholesome behaviours and to extend your life as far as possible. It is also for those you know and love so that you enjoy life with them as much as possible, having made conscious decisions so that you are more active. Above all, it is in recognition that you are the steward of your body, honouring the Creator in looking after it well so that you can serve Him.

ACTION POINT

- *Reduce and then eliminate processed sugars from your diet.*

NOTES

1 World Health Organisation (WHO), 'WHO calls on countries to reduce sugars intake among adults and children', 4 March 2015, http://www.who.int/mediacentre/news/releases/2015/sugar-guideline/en/

2 Ken Peeters et al, 'Fructose-1,6-bisphosphate couples glycolytic flux to activation of Ras', *Nature Communications*, Issue 8, 922, 13 October 2017 https://www.nature.com/articles/s41467-017-01019-z

3 Susan Sloane, 'Why does high (or low) blood sugar give me headaches?' *Diabetic Connect*, http://www.diabeticconnect.com/diabetes-information-articles/general/338-are-your-blood-sugar-levels-giving-you-headaches [accessed 5 April 2018]

4 Sarika Arora, 'Is sugar sabotaging your hormones?', *Women's Health Network*, https://www.womenshealthnetwork.com/hormonalimbalance/hormonal-imbalance-caused-by-sugar.aspx [accessed 5 April 2018]

5 *Dietary Guidelines for Americans,* https://health.gov/dietaryguidelines/dga95/9dietgui.htm [accessed 5 April 2018]

6   Lisa Te Morengo, Simonette Mallard and Jim Mann, 'Dietary sugars and body weight: systematic review and meta-analysis of randomised controlled trials and cohort studies', *British Medical Journal*, January 2013, p. 346, https://www.bmj.com/content/346/bmj.e7492?view=long&pmid=23321486

7   James E Gangwisch et al, 'High glycaemic index diet as a risk factor for depression: analyses from the Women's Health Initiative', *The American Journal of Clinical Nutrition*, 102 (2), 1 August 2015, 454–463, https://academic.oup.com/ajcn/article/102/2/454/4564524

8   Sara Lindberg, '7 scary things that can happen to your body if you eat too much processed food', *Insider*, 5 February 2019, https://www.msn.com/en-za/health/nutrition/7-scary-things-that-can-happen-to-your-body-if-you-eat-too-much-processed-food/ar-BBThvYS

9   Anika Knüppel et al, 'Sugar Intake from sweet food and beverages, common mental disorder and depression: prospective findings from the Whitehall II study', *Scientific Reports*, Issue 7,2017, Article 6287, https://www.nature.com/articles/s41598-017-05649-7

10 See, for example, 'Higher brain glucose levels may mean more severe Alzheimer's', *National Institute on Aging* (NIA), 6 November 2017, https://www.nih.gov/news-events/news-releases/higher-brain-glucose-levels-may-mean-more-severe-alzheimers

11 Juliana F W Cohen, et al, 'Associations of Prenatal and Child Sugar Intake with Child Cognition', *American Journal of Preventative Medicine*, June 2018, 54 (6), 727–735, https://www.ajpmonline.org/article/S0749-3797(18)31606-4/fulltext

12 Sara Lindberg, '7 scary things that can happen to your body if you eat too much processed food', *Insider*, 5 February 2019, https://www.msn.com/en-za/health/nutrition/7-scary-things-that-can-happen-to-your-body-if-you-eat-too-much-processed-food/ar-BBThvYS

13 Alicia Kucharska, Agnieszka Szmurlo and Beata Sinska, 'Significance of diet in treated and untreated acne vulgaris', *Advances in Dermatology and Allergology*, April 2016, 33 (2): 81–85 https://www.ncbi.nlm.nih.gov/pmc/articles/PMC4884775/; H P Nguyen and R Katta, 'Sugar Sag: Glycation and the Role of Diet in Aging Skin', *Skin Therapy Letters*, November 2015,

20 (^): 1–5 https://pubmed.ncbi.nlm.nih.gov/27224842/

14   See, for example, Martin G Myers Jr, Rudolph L Leibel, Randy J Seeley and Michael W Schwartz, 'Obesity and leptin resistance: distinguishing cause from effect', *Trends in Endocrinology & Metabolism*, November 2010, 21 (11), 643–651, https://www.sciencedirect.com/science/article/pii/S1043276010001323

15   Scott M Grundy, 'Hypertriglyceridemia, insulin resistance, and the metabolic syndrome', *The American Journal of Cardiology*, 13 May 1999, 83 (9), Supplement 2, 25–29, https://www.sciencedirect.com/science/article/pii/S00029149990021185

16   Sanjay Basu et al, 'The Relationship of Sugar to Population-Level Prevalence: An Economic Analysis of Repeated Cross-Sectional Data', *PLOS One*, 27 February 2013, http://journals.plos.org/plosone/article?id=10.1371/journal.pone.005787; 3

17   See, for example, Shira Zelbar-Sagi et al, 'Long term nutritional intake and the risk for non-alcoholic fatty liver disease (NAFLD): A population based study', *Journal of Hepatology*, 47 (5), November 2007, 711–S717, https://www.sciencedirect.com/science/article/pii/S0168827807004278

18   Sara Lindberg, '7 scary things that can happen to your body if you eat too much processed food', *Business Insider Australia*, https://www.businessinsider.com.au/processed-foods-affect-on-body-2019-2

19   David A Shohan et al, 'Sugary Soda Consumption and Albuminuria: Results from the National health and Nutrition Examination Survey, 1999–2004', *PLOS One*, 17 October 2008, http://journals.plos.org/plosone/article?id=10.1371/journal.pone.0003431

20   Hyon K Choi and Gary Curhan, 'Soft drinks, fructose consumption, and the risk of gout in men: prospective cohort study', *British Medical Journal*, February 2008, p. 336, https://www.bmj.com/content/336/7639/309

21   Marilda Mazzali et al, 'Elevated Uric Acid Increases Blood Pressure in the Rat by a Novel Crystal-Independent Mechanism', *Hypertension*, 1 November 2001, issue 38, pp. 1101–1106, http://hyper.ahajournals.org/content/38/5/11010

22   Charlotte El Evans et al, 'Glycaemic index, glycaemic load, and blood pressure: a systemic review and meta-analysis of randomized controlled

trials', *American Journal of Clinical Nutrition*, May 2017, 105 (5): 1176–1190 https://pubmed.ncbi.nlm.nih.gov/28404579/

23 Quanhe Yang et al, 'Added Sugar Intake and Cardiovascular Disease Mortality Among US Adults', *JAMA Internal Medicine*, April 2014, 174 issue (4), 516–524, https://jamanetwork.com/journals/jamainternalmedicine/fullarticle/1819573https://jamanetwork.com/journals/jamainternalmedicine/fullarticle/1819573

24 R Freeman, 'Moderate evidence support a relationship between sugar intake and dental caries', *Evidence Based Dentistry*, 15, (4), December 2014, 98–99, https://www.ncbi.nlm.nih.gov/pubmed/25522936

25 Vanessa Muirhead et al, 'Oral health in community pharmacy—Raising awareness of oral health and pain management for children and young people' (*Community Pharmacy Public Health Campaign and Additional Audit*, November 2016) https://www.myhealth.london.nhs.uk/sites/default/files/Community%20pharmacy%20oral%20health%20campaign%20-%20Nov%202016.pdf

26 PHE figures were cited in: Amy Packham, 'A Child in England Has a Tooth Removed in Hospital Every 10 Minutes Due to Preventable Decay', *Huffington Post UK*, 6 April 2018, https://www.huffingtonpost.co.uk/entry/child-tooth-decay-preventable_uk_5ac5ec23e4b056a8f59886ed

27 NN Nwiizu et al, 'Periodontal Disease and Incident Cancer Risk among Postmenopausal Women: results from the Women's Health Initiative Observational Cohort', *Cancer Epidemiology, Biomarkers and Prevention*, August 2017, 26 (8), 1255–1265

28 'The Beginner's Guide to Cutting out Sugar', https://www.wellandgood.com/good-food/beginners-guide-to-cutting-out-sugar/

7 Healthy eating

For everything God created is good, and nothing is to be rejected if it is received with thanksgiving, because it is consecrated by the word of God and prayer (1 Timothy 4:4–5).

In his book on finding communities that live the longest (commonly called 'blue zones'), one of the discoveries that Dan Buettner made was that they eat predominantly plant-based diets, which feature leafy greens and legumes in great amounts. Beans are regarded as a great source of protein.

He wrote: 'Beans (legumes) also provide a cornerstone to the Blue Zones diet. Diets rich in legumes are associated with fewer heart attacks and less colon cancer. Legumes are a good dietary source of healthy flavonoids and fibre (which can reduce the risk of heart attack) and are also an excellent nonanimal source of protein.'[1]

Another person who found benefit from studying how other people lived was John Day, a cardiologist. His conclusion was: 'Processed foods and added sugar have never shown to have a health benefit. Cutting them out is 90 per cent of a healthy diet right there.'[2]

In these two quotes are the reasons why we should be cutting out processed foods (where the benefits of the ingredients have been eradicated) and start eating the natural goodness that God has provided for us.

Emotions

Eating more fruit and vegetables is not only good for us physically—

it also affects us emotionally. It has been ascertained that an increased consumption of these resulted in increased happiness, life satisfaction and wellbeing.

Increasing your intake of fruit and vegetables to ten portions a day has the equivalent life satisfaction points of moving from unemployment to employment—it is truly a transforming phenomenon. The advantage is that, while the benefits of eating fruit and vegetables may only be observed decades later, the wellbeing improvements are observable more immediately.[3]

In the short-term, we have all found that it is easily done to go on vacation or attend a celebration and come back with 'holiday fat' as we 'treat' ourselves with high calories, high fat and sugar content (with no health value at all), coupled with little or no activity. We need to be aware that the body can stand two days of eating all the wrong food, but five days of nutritional abuse will alter its metabolism—so a long weekend of bodily abuse by ourselves can be tolerated, but any longer will have a greater impact. The result of this, regardless of the number of days that we relax our dietary regime, is that we will become less able to process sugar efficiently, so the effective way of absorbing calories for future use will be disrupted. The net outcome will be a path from relaxation and letting go to obesity and excess weight, and its associated dangers such as diabetes, strokes and heart disease.[4]

A reason why we are so reluctant to exercise after we have been on holiday is because, as has been noted before, the increase in weight is a precursor to the unwillingness to be involved in physical activity. We would have got out of the routine and most probably suffer with a mental block, causing a reluctance to get back onto the treadmill (or whatever our preferred method of physical activity happens to be). I often find that my exercise regime can be hit and miss, particularly during the holiday period, and that getting back into it afterwards can be a real struggle.

We can come back to a healthy way of living by selecting the right foodstuffs. As an example, it has been ascertained that the key foods to reduce neurogenerative and cardiovascular decline (such as hypertension, heart attack and stroke) are vegetables, berries, olive oil and fish; whilst red meat, cheese, butter, pastries, sweets, fried and fast food were to be avoided. It is important to take note of this fact as stroke survivors were two times more at risk of developing dementia compared to the general population.[5]

Eating on a budget

According to the Royal College of Paediatrics and Child Health (RCPCH), one in five primary school children are obese with those from poor families being affected the most. It found that 40 per cent of children from the most deprived areas were overweight or obese in comparison with 27 per cent of children in the most affluent areas. The health of Scottish children was discovered to be the worst in Europe.[6]

Across the age groups, research has estimated that, in the United Kingdom, 20 million people or four in ten (39 per cent) of the population stated that they could not afford healthy food. In the group of adults aged between 25 and 29 years, over half (58 per cent) stated that they could not afford to eat in a healthy way.

The main drivers away from eating healthily would appear to be the taste of healthy food (43 per cent), the cost involved (34 per cent) and the ease of availability and preparation (34 per cent). Indeed, nearly a fifth of the respondents to a survey (18 per cent) of those earning less than £20,000 said that cost was the most important driver for not eating healthy food, compared to half that number (8 per cent) of those people earning £40,000 and above.[7] The latter two factors in particular will affect those in low-wage households where the finances and time involved are of the uttermost importance—eating healthily does seem to come at a premium.

It is important as poor diet is now the major contributing factor for more deaths than smoking globally.[8]

It has been stated that: 'Our weight is largely determined by our environmental circumstances and how we respond to a backdrop of cheap food, persistent advertising, living in areas of fast-food retailers, and where high-sugar, processed food is plentiful.'[9]

The main advice given by the UK Government is[10]:

- Eat at least ten portions of a variety of fruit and vegetables a day.
- Base our meals on vegetables and starchy carbohydrates, such as potatoes, bread, rice, pasta should take up no more than a third to a quarter of the plate, choosing wholegrain where possible.
- Have some dairy or dairy alternatives (such as soya drinks and yoghurts). Choose lower fat and lower-sugar options.
- Eat some beans, pulses, fish, eggs, meat and other protein. Aim for at least two portions of fish every week, one of which should be oily, such as salmon or mackerel.

- Choose unsaturated oils and spreads; and eat in small amounts.

The problem is often that the cost of purchasing items that are full of protein can be prohibitive for families with low incomes. However, it has been ascertained that the best sources for those families on a budget are:

- Kidney beans
- Pinto beans
- Whole chicken
- Chickpeas
- Tuna (tinned)

A tin of red kidney beans (in water) is the cheapest source of protein, compared to the most expensive being beef (rump steak).[11] With the use of canned and frozen food, a healthy meal can be made to fill up the stomach and also give energy for activity.

The cost of tuna with a jacket potato, or beans and pulses in a chilli con carne, means that a nutritious meal can still be within the means of most people's budgets.

Portions

In addition to understanding what is good to eat, it is also important to know how big the portions should be. People can be perplexed as to why they do not lose weight when they are eating all the right products, but you only have to look at their plates to see that they are trying to eat all those good things that God has provided in one big go.

King Solomon illustrated what gorging on food looked like: 'In the house of the wise are stores of choice food and oil, but a foolish man devours all that he has' (Proverbs 21:20).

As a historical observation, it has been noted that, when the painted depictions of the Last Supper were analysed, the portrayals have shown increasingly larger servings as each artist has painted the event down through the ages—with each generation, the amounts have increased. When Jesus and the people of first century Galilee had a meal, the portions that they ate were modest by our twenty-first century standards because the land was used prudently to grow crops and to herd livestock, in comparison to the proliferate way that we now squeeze every possible drop of goodness from the globe.

The modern situation can be illustrated in pot-luck meals, or whatever name is given to them, where people all bring food for a communal feast. There are always individuals or families that are well-known for piling their plates so that it resembles the equivalent of a gastronomical Mount Everest. We need to hear the words of the Bible: 'He who keeps the law is a discerning son, but a companion of gluttons disgraces his father' (Proverbs 28:7). It is easy for the line between hospitality and sharing food to be breached so that it gives way to excessiveness.

Some individuals have practised this skill of ingenuity and excessiveness, so that they have become masters of the culinary pile-up. In a restaurant that was famed for a salad bar that could be accessed as often as needed, an individual was observed constructing a structure that was noticeable in its brilliance—starting with cucumber and other salad material to build up the walls, the lettuce gave the foundation, other items were carefully piled within and so the edifice was created.

Even when dishes are served at the table, the portion sizes have increased more markedly in the past fifty years, which may be an added pressure. When people are taught to politely eat all that is on their plate, it can be difficult to leave any food remaining. It has been considered that the larger the portion, the more people are likely to over-indulge, especially if the food is HFSS (high in fat, sugar and salt).

As we have already seen from the UK guidelines, we need ten portions of vegetables a day. When I am cooking, I try to place all of the portions on one plate in one sitting so I can be as guilty as anyone else in this respect!

Change in diet

Since 1975, the consumption of ready meals and processed meat has increased by five times. There are twenty-six times more pizzas being eaten and a three-times increase in the purchase of chips over the same time period. It is in contrast to the scepticism in the United Kingdom in the 1950s where even pizzas were regarded as an upmarket version of cheese on toast. The proliferation of pizza and other fast-food outlets on such a monumental scale is a recent phenomenon—there have been stalls that have sold pies in the medieval times, street food in Asia and so forth which continue this tradition, but never on such an industrial scale.

Our diets have altered to such an extent as illustrated by the fact that dried and fresh pasta was not noted on the UK's National Food Survey until 1998, and its consumption has more than doubled in the ensuing years. It has now become a de rigueur part of our diet; indeed, it not unusual to purchase gluten-free versions.

There has been an increase in the manufacture and marketing of 'sharing bags' of products such as crisps and chocolate. A result has been that 40 per cent of young people under the age of 25 years consume regularly a whole 150g sharing bag of crisps on one occasion, which is the equivalent of 750 calories and makes up about a third of an adult's recommended daily calorie intake. It is not to say that other age groups are innocent of such behaviour. There is some evidence that the increase in the mass-marketing of chocolate-sharing bags is the unintended result of the manufacturers deciding to phase out the king size products.

According to Public Health England, most adults are consuming 200 to 300 more calories a day than they need, with many being unsure how to calculate how much they should eat or drink.

In order to help people, PHE have devised the 400-600-600 rule of thumb, which equates to 400 calories for breakfast, 600 for lunch and 600 for dinner. It allows for a couple of healthy snacks and drinks in between as part of the balanced diet of 2,000 calories for women and 2,500 for men on a daily basis.[12]

Breakfast	Lunch	Dinner
400 kcal	600 kcal	600 kcal
And a couple of healthy snacks		

In order to help with maintaining a good diet, it is recommended that non-starchy vegetables could fill half of your plate as they are low in kilojoules and so reduce your calorific intake. They are also high in dietary fibre and nutrients which will help with your body's maintenance. There should be only one carbohydrate on one quarter of the plate, which can be chosen from potato, sweet potato, corn on the cob, quinoa, rice, pasta, couscous, legumes, wholegrain bread or cereals.[13]

Carbohydrates

There are three colours of carbohydrates: beige, white and green, so it also matters what the colour of the carbohydrate is as it is the beige-coloured and the white-coloured ones that need to be restricted.

The beige-coloured carbohydrates include what we normally understand by the term 'carbohydrates', with examples being bread, pasta, potatoes and rice.

The white-coloured carbohydrates include sugary foods like fizzy drinks, sweets, and processed and refined foods including cakes and biscuits.

In most of the beige- and white-coloured carbohydrates, much of the starch and sugar are broken down into glucose for energy. The result is that, if you eat too much white- or beige-coloured carbohydrate food, the glucose is stored as fat.

The table shown in Figure 2 (see p. 146) includes the recommended dietary requirements.

The third colour of carbohydrates is green, which is dietary fibre located in fruit and vegetables. These 'green carbs' ensures that the stomach is full, slowing its emptying, and contains vitamins and minerals.

While the majority of the plate can be filled with vegetables, the other quarter of the plate can be supplied with a source of protein

Reduce	Replace with	Include
Flour	Cauliflower rice	Eggs
Rice	Celeriac	Meat
Potatoes	Sweet potatoes	Fish
Pasta	Rye or pumpernickel	Nuts
Breakfast cereals	bread	Legumes
Other processed grains		Half each dish should be green or brightly coloured: fresh vegetables, salad greens, tomatoes and aubergines

Figure 2

such as a meat substitute (such as Quorn or soya), chicken or fish. On infrequent occasions, a reasonably sized portion of red meat (such as pork, beef or lamb) can be included.

Another element to consider is to include resistant starch (found in high-fibre foods such as lentils, beans and unprocessed grains) that feeds the gut bacteria in the colon (the lower digestive tract). It will enable the healthy bacteria in that part of the body to thrive in order to defeat the bacteria that will cause illness.

An interesting tip is that reheating food with bad carbohydrates changes their composition so that they turn into good. If starches (such as pasta and toasted bread from the freezer) are reheated, the molecules are reconfigured and become more resistant, so travelling down the gut to feed the microbiome.[14]

Benefits

Just by doing this one action of reducing calorie-intake, it is possible to prevent or at least postpone the onset of many age-related conditions. Over a period of one year, people who reduced their calories saw their biological age increase by 0.11 years, whereas the control group had a rise of 0.71 years, so showing the slowing down of the ageing process. [15]

It has also been ascertained that if the calorific intake was reduced by 15 per cent, a person's life expectancy could be extended.

It is not only in the future that there are advantages, but also in the shorter term as the process of eating less slows down the metabolism, which indicates that the body is utilising the received fuel more effectively. In addition, the oxidative stress is lessened, so reducing the possibility of cancer, diabetes and Alzheimer's Disease. [16]

The thought that we are eating healthily albeit with more on our plates may give us a false sense of security. If we are eating large portions of health foods, we can be eating more calories than someone else who is tucking into a chocolate bar. It is especially true where foods such as nut butters, seeds, avocados and salmon are healthy options, as they are also high in calories. It makes sense to use a weighing machine and other kitchen utensils (such as a spaghetti measurer) to ensure that the correct sized portion is consumed. Otherwise, there could be an increase in weight rather than a reduction because your body is taking in more calories than is required. [17]

Types of fat

Fats store energy and manages hormones, especially those concerning our metabolism, which indicates that the types of fat we have already will influence how much more we will accumulate and where it will be stored.[18]

Generally speaking, the darker the fats are, the better it is for you as the white fats will cause the longer-term issues.

Brown fat (also known as brown adipose tissue (BAT))—provides cellular energy and assists in reducing weight through exercising. It also controls our core temperature. It is located in the back of the neck and chest areas. This type of fat can be increased by healthy lifestyle and assists in reducing diabetes risk.

Beige Fat—is a combination of white and brown fat and is located along the spine and collarbone. When exercise is undertaken, the hormone irisin is released to convert the white fat to beige fat. Certain foods, such as grapes, can also assist in this process.

White subcutaneous fat—stores calories and produces the hormone adiponectin, which enables the liver and muscles to manage insulin. It also stabilises blood sugar level and manages the white fat stores. The difficulty arises when there is too much white fat, which results in excessive secretion of adiponectin, so that the metabolism is decelerated, and the result is excess weight (particularly in the hip, thigh and stomach area—the most stubborn areas to lose the weight).

Subcutaneous fat (SF)—is immediately under the skin of our bodies, but particularly in the back of our arms, thighs and buttocks. It is the measurement of this fat that determines our body fat percentage. It produces the oestrogen hormone in both sexes where, if too much subcutaneous fat is produced, oestrogen will become dominant and cause toxic weight gain.

Visceral fat—is the white fat that can be dangerous as it is accumulates around the abdomen. The indicators can be an enlarged stomach and inflamed liver caused by the blood, drained from the fat around the organs, being 'dumped' there. The symptoms can be seen in increased blood cholesterol levels, together with inflammatory chemicals that could result in heart disease, Type 2 diabetes and cancer. Where this type of fat is in healthy proportions, it is good for your overall health as it cushions our organs and stabilises our core temperatures.

Fat can be good news

Fat is in itself not a bad thing as it contains a type of immune cell called immune T cell, which learns to fight infection from previous exposure to pathogens. It means these cells stored in the fat tissue— which acts as a reservoir and activator—have an important role as they confront the pathogens more strongly.

While it is beneficial to have some body fat, there is still a detrimental effect to being overweight. We can fool ourselves into thinking that we can carry some and can get rid of it when we like. The reality is that the fat stays firmly on our bodies and we have to be dedicated through healthy eating and exercise in order to remove it.

The calories you need

It has been assumed, down through the generations, that the average woman requires 2,000 while the requirement for the average man is 2,500 calories,

However, the situation is more complex as it depends on your height, mobility and the activity of your metabolism as well as other factors such as pregnancy.

It is necessary to calculate the Basal Metabolic Rate (BMR)

utilising the Schofield Calculator described in figure 3, which calculates the number of calories you need if you were to lie in bed all day.

The appropriate age bracket needs to be picked before your scales tell you your exact weight in kilogrammes (W).

Males	Females
10–17 Years BMR = 17.7 x W + 657 SEE = 105	10–17 Years BMR = 13.4 x W + 692 SEE = 112
18–29 Years BMR = 15.1 x W + 692 SEE = 156	18–29 Years BMR = 14.8 x W + 487 SEE = 120
30–59 Years BMR = 11.5 x W + 873 SEE = 167	30–59 Years BMR = 8.3 x W + 846 SEE = 112

Figure 3

The Standard Error of Estimation (SEE) is the means of rectifying the number of calories out in either direction. It could be that the person is very muscular and has more lean weight than the average person, so the SEE value has to be added.[19]

In addition to calculating the BMR, a person's Physical Activity Level (PAL) or Physical Activity Factor (PAF) has also to be factored in.

PHYSICAL ACTIVITY LEVEL (PAL)/PHYSICAL ACTIVITY FACTOR (PAF)	
Men	**Women**
BMR x 1.4 inactive	BMR x 1.4 inactive
BMR x 1.7 moderately active	BMR x 1.6 moderately active
BMR x 1.9 very active	BMR x 1.8 very active

The definitions are as follows:

Inactive—This would be a person in non-physically demanding work, such as at a desk. There would be no structured exercise and their lifestyle would be low intensity.

Moderate—This person would be in a more physically demanding job, such as one that requires much walking. There would also be some structured, moderately intensive exercise about three times a week.

Very active—There would be intense exercise one hour a day, or a person whose job was very physically demanding (such as in heavy industry) and also undertook some structured exercise.

Children and young people require more calories as they require the boost in their bodily growth and development. Regarding the genders, men require more calories than women because their muscle mass has to have more calories to maintain it. It still does not mean that there is any excuse for over-indulging.

The consumption of calories also depends on the season of life. For example, women can take on extra calories to enable the growth of her unborn baby and in the production of breast milk compared to other times in her life. Another example would be elderly people who need the extra nourishment for their bodies to function (their diets tend to be high in sugars and fats), so the menu in a care home will have more calories (such as the inclusion of full fat milk) than what is usually required outside of this setting.

Snacks

If snacks and treats are going to be part of the household, it would be a good idea to have them out of sight. If the goodies are in open view, it is more of a temptation to devour them.

Like many households, we can have things like chocolate hidden away in a drawer, where they can remain for days and weeks. However, once they are opened, there is the unhealthy prospect of being rapidly eaten—just because they are there!

The healthier option is not to have them in the house at all. If snacks are to be present then substitutes like nuts or carrot sticks, eaten with hummus, could be included, although the amount of these should be monitored because, despite being sources of good fat and necessary vitamins, too many can also result in weight being put on.

Processed meat

The eating of processed meat can have an adverse effect on a person's cholesterol, with the subsequent consequences such as heart attacks and strokes. However, in addition, the World Health Organisation has classified salted, cured and fermented meat as being a source of bowel cancer.[20]

There is also a risk of eating processed meats, such as sausages and bacon, increasing the risk of breast cancer in older women. It could even account for one in six cases of the disease, which could have been avoidable.

The example was given of middle-aged women who ate more than 9g of sausages and bacon in a day. In this scenario, they were approximately 20 per cent more likely to develop breast cancer than those who avoided processed meat.

If women in this age group ate small portions of processed meats on an infrequent basis, they were still 15 per cent more likely to develop breast cancer.

A caution has to be issued because in younger women, there was no connection between processed meats and breast cancer.[21]

Dr Jasmine Just from Cancer Research UK commented that: 'Eating a lot of processed meat does increase the risk of bowel cancer though, so while the odd salami sandwich won't do much harm, it's still a good idea to cut down where you can.'[22]

Salt

Salt is one of the predominant features of our convenience and fast-food products. It is not surprising that we often feel thirsty after consuming such food in order for our bodies to deal with this substance.

Despite the numerous warnings from the medical authorities about the risk of hypertension (high blood pressure) and its consequences, there is still a tendency to put too much salt on our food. Although it is well-know that too much of this substance can increase the risk of developing hypertension and cardiac conditions, it has also been ascertained that it can adversely affect the neurons in the brain, resulting in cognitive conditions, such as dementia.

It is the result of a reduced blood flow to the brain as a consequence of the immune system in the gut being affected. When we cease having a high-salt diet, it is possible for the blood flow and neuron function to return to its normal levels.[23]

Eating in the evening

It is possible to restrict your eating throughout the day, carefully avoiding the tempting snacks and high-calorific drinks, only to succumb in the evening. As you possibly get in late from a hard day's work or the strain of caring for a loved one (whether children or aging parents), the defences seem to readily crumble. It could very well be down to your hormones that you fail at the late hours.

It was discovered that, after a stressful day, people are hungrier in the evening than in the morning. Levels of ghrelin, the hormone that stimulates the appetite, were found to be higher after the ingesting of an afternoon meal in comparison to that after a morning meal, while levels of the PYY hormone (responsible for reducing appetite) were lower in the evening.

As people get stressed, their ghrelin levels increase in proportion. The evidence suggests that the stress experienced throughout the day has a major influence on our hormone level in the evening. In other words, if we have had a stressful day, we are more prone to eat too much in the evening.

The research report states: 'Eating late in the day is common, and stress can induce eating ... Afternoon/evening may be a high-risk period for overeating, particularly when paired with stress exposure, and for those with binge eating.'[24]

There is truth in the adage: Breakfast like a king, lunch like a lord and dinner like a pauper.

The implication is that steps can be taken to reduce the risk of overeating by eating earlier in the day or by finding alternative ways of dealing with stress, such as talking to a counsellor or other trained person.

Breakfast

In one report, more than a quarter of adults admitted to missing breakfast, with one in four in the 21–34 age group missing breakfast most of the time. This age group was also the one most likely to miss lunch.[25]

Another study found that the people who missed breakfast were at greater risk of experiencing the early stages of atherosclerosis (a build-up of fatty tissue within the arteries) compared to those who ate a high-energy breakfast, which provides 20 per cent of a person's daily energy intake. Indeed, the researchers came to the conclusion that those who missed this meal were likely to have unhealthy lifestyles, with this group having the larger waist circumferences, body mass indices and higher blood pressures.

The adverse effects of skipping breakfast can be seen early in childhood in the form of childhood obesity and, although breakfast skippers are generally attempting to lose weight, those people often end up eating more and unhealthier foods later in the day.

It is salutary to know that skipping breakfast can cause hormonal imbalances and alter circadian rhythms. That breakfast is the most important meal of the day has been proven right in the light of this evidence.[26]

It is an important message because parents of obese children were twice as likely to state that their children did not eat breakfast compared to those with normal weight children. In turn, in relation to the parent's employment status, it was in households where the parents were not working that children were less likely to eat that important first meal.

In contrast, if we eat a fibre-rich breakfast every day, which has positive influences on the intestinal bacteria in the gut, we reduce our risk of developing rheumatoid arthritis. This condition is an autoimmune disease that causes pain, swelling and stiffness in the joints with the most impact usually being in the hands, feet and wrists. Hence, from the start of each day, you can be setting yourself up for the possibility of a healthy future.

In addition, such a diet can assist in the development of stronger bones, with better bone density, so having implications of reducing the risk of conditions such as osteoporosis (which may impact many women after the menopause).[27]

It is the process of eating fibre-rich food each morning as well as enough fruit and vegetables throughout the day that will help to maintain a rich variety of bacterial species.'[28]

Health foods

There must be consideration when eating what are considered to be health foods, as there can be hidden dangers. An example is that Public Health England revealed children's yoghurts can contain nearly their total daily allowance of sugar, with some products having almost five cubes worth of sugar in them.[29] When you are searching for a low-fat yoghurt, for example, look at the sugar content because it is often increased to improve the taste, making up for the fat deficiency.

The key to the matter is to find a product that is reduced in both fat and sugar, and to eat it in moderate portions.

Television advertisements

When we are watching commercial stations that garner revenue from advertising slots, we would do well to be out of the room when food is the subject of these advertisements or (possibly a better suggestion) we could record the whole programme so that we can skip over these tempting advertisements.

When we think that we feel the sensation of hunger, it is often mistaken for the reality that we are actually thirsty, so the best option is to remove ourselves from the room in order to put the kettle on for a drink, if we are unable to fast-forward the adverts.

The reason why they are successful in persuading us is because they convince us that we are hungry even though we are not. The same logic goes that we are hungrier when viewing cooking programmes, even to the extent of consuming ready-made meals while being instructed on how to cook nutritious cuisine by top-rated chefs.

Mindful eating

Conversely, one of the reasons why people can overeat is because they are being distracted by, for example, television or other gadgets—they are not interacting with the contents on the plate.

It could be that the mind is set on the computer or television screen before them, especially if it is an enthralling puzzle or a box set. The temptation is then to keep delving into the snack bowl in front without considering how much has been consumed.

A consequence can be eating too much, as there is not alertness to the stomach's acknowledgement to the brain that it has had sufficient. There can also be symptoms such as heart burn, stomach cramps and hiccups as you are not eating with the right posture, gulping down the meal and not chewing with thoroughness.[30]

It could be rectified by the simple act of putting your knife and fork, or spoon, down between each mouthful in order to allow your body to digest what you have just eaten. It will also ensure that you are not gulping air along with the food, which can cause flatulence, or that your diaphragm is not out of sync, which will cause hiccups.

There is no reason why you have to clean the plate if you are fully satisfied, yet we often carry on regardless because we are not concentrating on what we are doing. It is also alright to say 'no' when offered seconds—you are not on a mission to consume the world's store! When you first decline that second helping or acknowledge that the portion was too big, you might feel awkward, but continual practice will make it easier.

Research has indicated that eating slowly, not having after-dinner snacks and not eating within two hours of bedtime helped with reducing weight, obesity and waistlines.

In particular, the participants in the study who ate at the normal rate were 29 per cent less likely to be obese than those who ate quickly. For those who ate slowly, the comparison was greater as they were 42 per cent less likely to be obese than the quick eaters. The waist size was noticeably smaller among those who ate at a normal or slow speed.

The rapid eating of food has been associated with impaired glucose intolerance and insulin resistance, which may lead to diabetes. It could have the effect of preventing weight loss as the message is not getting to the brain from the stomach that it is full. For slower eaters, the message of satiety between the two organs is given time to register before an excess amount of food is eaten, so less calories are consumed.[31]

When we are not thinking about what we are eating, we often fail to make it a social occasion (bearing in mind that the word 'company' is derived from the phrase 'with bread') and we are not giving due regard to the good provisions that God has given to us, despite having said grace beforehand. We may also be surrounded by friends and family but not be interacting with them because we are so determined to finish our meal as quickly as possible—by not stopping to communicate we are not fully benefitting from the food or the friendship.

The incentive

In his assessment of happiness, Robert Lustig recognises cooking as one of the 'c's (along with connecting, contributing and coping) that would work towards that objective.[32] He comments on the modern diet: 'There are three items in food that have to do with pleasure verses happiness ... Number one is tryptophan, which is the precursor to serotonin. It's the rarest amino acid in the diet. You find it in eggs, some in poultry, and maybe a little in fish. Number two is omega-3 fatty acids, which are anti-inflammatory ... Finally, fructose depletes serotonin, ups your dopamine, and causes metabolic syndrome—it's a total disaster.'

He continued in his assessment with a dissecting analysis of the modern reliance on processed food, which is low in tryptophan, low in omega-3s, and high in fructose. He continued: 'It's the antithesis of contentment. But 33 per cent of Americans don't know how to cook, and if you don't know how to cook, you're hostage to the food industry your entire life.'[33]

We are to unlock the chains that bind us to the lure of processed and fast food with the key to all the good nutritious ingredients that God has provided. We can be so addicted to the beckoning of the television or the smart phone that we can forget we have kitchens, often filled with unused or rarely used utensils. Our great Creator wants us to join Him in being creative, albeit in a small but satisfying way by utilising what He has given to us.

Repairing the damage

It was discovered that adults who ate a diet consisting of two tomatoes and more than three portions of apples daily experienced a slower decline in lung function over ten years than those who ate less than these allocations, and the nutrients even repaired any damage that had been done. However, it was necessary to consume fresh fruit as canned or processed tomatoes and apples did not have the same result.[34]

In contrast, the calories in sweetened beverages, including those in soft drinks, can be harmful to our health in particular.

An example was that a 12-ounce (340 ml) can of a sugary soft drink was very much less healthy than a medium-sized potato, even though the latter is high in starch. The former can induce a higher risk of cardiovascular disease and Type 2 diabetes; the latter is full of potassium and fibre so giving numerous nutritional benefits.

The calories contained within sweetened beverages have the potential to increase the risk for obesity and cardiometabolic disease because all calories can directly contribute to positive energy balance and fat gain.

In addition, the consumption of a certain amount of calories from fructose-sweetened drinks with a high level of fructose corn syrup can lead to higher risks of cardiac disease or stroke, whereas the same number of calories from sources such as yoghurt and cheese can have the opposite effect.

Likewise, with regard to fat content, foods with high amounts of polyunsaturated fat (e.g. chai seeds and nuts) reduces the risk of disease, compared the increased risk caused by the same portion of saturated fat (e.g. in red meat).[35]

There is no reason why we cannot repair the damage that we are doing to our bodies by commencing better eating habits now.

Diets

In the western world, in particular, there are a whole host of diets that can be followed, such as Atkins, Dukan, Keto, cabbage soup (or any other based on one food stuff like potatoes or bananas), 5.2, Weight Watchers (WW), Slimming World and the list continues. It seems as though the more affluent we are, the more varied diets are available to rectify our weight problem. It has been calculated that two-thirds of people in the UK are dieting 'most of the time' with British women spending seventeen years of their lives on diets.

Rhiannon Lambert, a Harley Street nutritionist, urged people not to participate in dieting schemes as they do not work. She added: 'Dieting often includes restriction, be it a low carbohydrate intake, low fat intake or meal replacements.

'It's widely understood that by restricting certain food groups in our diet, in particular carbohydrates, it can often lead to enhanced sugar cravings which may result in a vicious cycle of binging and restricting. Needless to say, this way of eating also encourages an unhealthy relationship with food which may lead to disordered eating conditions.

'Also, by becoming engrossed in counting calories and restricting our food intake, which is often a requirement of most diets, it means becoming more and more confused as to what it means to be healthy.'[36]

It is true that dieting to the extremes can cause the body to cling to fat cells and cease muscle growth, as the body thinks that it is going into a famine situation. It is best to undertake any weight-loss diet under supervision, either medical or a recognised organisation.

It can be of assistance that, instead of subscribing to a diet regime, you are to focus on a lifestyle change that can alter your life. One such example is the 80/20 principle that will avoid the dangers of concentrating too much on what you are eating. The concept is that, for 80 per cent of the time, the consumables will be healthy and, for the remaining 20 per cent, the food and drink will be anything that you want. The calculation is that if a person eats three square meals a day for a week, 3 of the 21 meals in the week can be 'cheat' meals. If a person consumes five small meals a day for a week, 7 of the 35 small meals in the week can be 'cheat' meals.

Moreover, it has been proven that the most successful way to reduce weight is to regularly share the highs and the lows with friends, family and online followers. It includes the sharing of photos on social media. The regular sharing of a person's food journey assists in faster weight loss and is instrumental in keeping the lower weight when it is reached.[37] The diagnosis, whatever scheme is chosen, is that there needs to be community we can go to, so that we can also be encouraged along the journey.

It is in this community setting that there can be found the mixture of responsibility and accountable. However, ultimately, it is up to us as individuals to lose the weight and live healthy lives. Although, as Christians, we do have an advantage if our minds are being transformed by the Holy Spirit. It is also God's plan that we live in His community, the Church, in order that we can encourage and be encouraged as we seek to live healthily for Him.

Improved memory

It has been found that Mediterranean diets have the added advantage of boosting attention span and combatting cognitive decline.[38] As we seek to be effective for God's Kingdom, we should take useful steps to maintain our mental faculties.

Less cravings

When we eat in a healthy manner, we will find that our desire for unhealthy options will diminish.

Interestingly, eating spinach is helpful in suppressing appetite and the longing for food. A membrane found in the food, thylakoids, was responsible for ensuring people feel less hungry.

Assistance

We have already seen that people, particularly in lower socio-economic groups, may have difficulty in obtaining foodstuffs that are healthy.

There is the provision of foodbanks in the United Kingdom where churches and others can deposit long-lasting tins and cartons. We do have an obligation under God to care for those who are unable to provide for themselves, regardless of the reason.

It is also important that people seek assistance from their General Practitioners and nutritionists for any help that can provided. It will often be the case that medical authorities need to make a referral in order for people to obtain assistance from places such as the previously mentioned foodbanks and other food-assistance centres.

The Church also has an opportunity to serve those who are unable to provide healthy food for themselves, which includes the giving of hospitality. It is no coincidence that the word translated as 'hospitality' actually means 'love of the stranger' in the New Testament Greek language.

It is evident that we should do so for fellow Christians as we are told: 'Share with God's people who are in need. Practise hospitality' (Romans 12:13). The Scripture tells us that showing hospitality was the sign of a worthy widow (1 Timothy 5:9–10) and of a person who was to be an overseer in the local church (1 Timothy 3:2).

However, hospitality should also be given to those outside of the church. Indeed, it will be doing our service to Jesus as He said, 'For I was hungry and you gave me something to eat. I was thirsty and you gave me something to drink. I was a stranger and you invited me in' (Matthew 25:35).

We might be surprised in the final reckoning as to who we have welcomed into our homes: 'Do not forget to entertain strangers, for by so doing some people have entertained angels without knowing it' (Hebrews 13:2).

There is a warning that we are not to be begrudging or reticent in serving those, who may not be able to feed themselves, with nutritious food. Peter looks through our motives and declares: 'Offer hospitality to one another without grumbling' (1 Peter 4:9).

Saying thanks to God

When we say thanks to God, we need to make sure that what we are eating is suitable for the bodies that He has created. In the beginning, God created everything and referred to it as being good (Genesis 1:31). It is unavoidable to miss the fact that we have misused what He has made for our benefit. Paul urged us to consider: 'Whether we eat or drink or whatever you do, do it all for the glory of God' (1 Corinthians 10:31). If we are eating unhealthily, how can we honestly say that we are consuming in a way that will glorify God?

ACTION POINTS

- *Change your diet to be more like those in the 'blue zone'.*
- *Consider your portion sizes and reduce if necessary.*
- *Cook more often from scratch and enjoy God's provisions.*
- *Ensure you have breakfast.*
- *Eat slowly and purposefully remembering that God gave each morsel.*

NOTES

1 Dan Buettner, *The Blue Zones: 9 Lessons for Living Longer and the People Who've Lived the Longest*, (Washington D C: National Geographic Books, 2008) p. 276

2 Emily Laurence, 'The foods to eat daily for a super-long life (according to the oldest people in the world)', 17 July 2017, https://www.wellandgood.com/good-food/what-to-eat-for-long-life/. See John D Day and Jane Ann Day, *The Longevity Plan—Seven Life-Transforming Lessons from Ancient China* (London: HarperCollins Publishers, 2017)

3 Redzo Mujcic and Andrew J Oswald, 'Evolution of Well-Being and Happiness After Increases in Consumption of Fruit and Vegetables', *American Journal of Public Health*, 11 July 2016, 106 (8), 1504–1510, https://ajph.aphapublications.org/doi/pdf/10.2105/AJPH.2016.303260

4 Angela S Anderson et al, 'Early skeletal muscle adaptations to short-term

high-fat diet in humans before changes in insulin sensitivity', *Obesity*, 23 (4), 27 March 2015, pp. 720–724, https://onlinelibrary.wiley.com/doi/epdf/10.1002/oby.21031

5   Rachel Hosie, 'Mind diet: Medical researchers reveal new eating plan to combat cognitive decline', *The Independent*, 25 January 2018, https://www.independent.co.uk/life-style/health-and-families/mind-diet-cognitive-decline-food-latest-rush-university-medical-centre-a8177466.html

6   'Poverty in the UK jeopardising children's health, warns landmark report', *The Guardian*, 25 January 2017, https://www.theguardian.com/society/2017/jan/25/poverty-in-the-uk-jeopardising-childrens-health-warns-landmark-report

7   Based on Office for National Statistics numbers in: Rose Lasko-Skinner, *Turning the tables—Making healthy choices easier for consumers* (London: Demos, August 2020) p. 7

8   GBD 2017 Diet Contributors, 'Healthy effects of dietary risks in 195 countries, 1990–2017: a systemic analysis for the Global Burden of Disease', *The Lancet*, 2017, pp. 1958–1972   https://www.thelancet.com/journals/lancet/article/PIIS0140-6736(19)30041-8/fulltext

9   Abigail Scott Paul, 'Effective poverty and obesity campaigns need more than just stats', *Joseph Rowntree Foundation blog*, 9 May 2018, https://www.jrf.org.uk/blog/effective-poverty-and-obesity-campaigns-need-more-just-stats?utm_medium=email&utm_campaign=JRF%20weekly%20round-up%20wc%207%20May%202018&utm_content=JRF%20weekly%20round-up%20wc%207%20May%202018+CID_e387b0af0ccd8824d807eedc6121ebf5&utm_source=Email%20marketing%20software&utm_term=Read%20blog

10   *NHS Eatwell Guide*, https://www.nhs.uk/Livewell/Goodfood/Pages/the-eatwell-guide.aspx

11   Thomas Church, 'How Low Income Families Can Tackle Childhood Obesity', *Huffington Post UK*, 26 February 2017, https://www.huffingtonpost.co.uk/thomas-church/how-low-income-families-c_b_14932602.html?utm_hp_ref=uk-fat

12   Katie Jones, 'This Healthy Eating Tip Will Help You Stay Within The

Recommended Daily Calorie Intake', *Red*, 6 March 2018, http://www.redonline.co.uk/health-self/nutrition/recommended-calorie-intake-per-meal

13 Erin Cook, 'How to monitor your weight without watching the scales', *Harper's Bazaar*, 16 August 2017, https://www.harpersbazaar.com/uk/beauty/fitness-wellbeing/news/a43279/how-to-monitor-your-weight-without-watching-the-scales/

14 Dr Xand van Tulleken, 'Why beige carbs are the ones to avoid', *BBC News*, 6 June 2018, https://www.bbc.co.uk/news/health/health-44368601

15 Daniel W Belsky et al, 'Change in the Rate of Biological Aging in Response to Calorific Restriction: CALERIE Biobank Analysis', *The Journals of Gerontology*, Series A 73 (1), 12 December 2017, pp. 4–10 https://academic.oup.com/biomedgerontology/article/73/1/4/3834057

16 Leanne M Redman et al, 'Metabolic Slowing and Reduced Oxidative Damage with Sustained Calorific Restriction Support the rate of Living and Oxidative Damage Theories of Aging', *Cell Metabolism*, 2018, pp. 1–11, http://www.cell.com/cell-metabolism/pdf/S1550-4131(18)30130-X.pdf

17 Olivia Petter, 'Overeating "healthy" foods can make you put on weight, claims dietician', *The Independent*, 16 April 2018, https://www.independent.co.uk/life-style/food-and-drink/healthy-foods-overeating-weight-gain-dietitian-almonds-chocolate-leanne-ward-a8306801.html

18 See Kim Easton-Smith, 'The 5 different types of body fat', *Cosmopolitan*, 19 July 2018, https://www.cosmopolitan.com/uk/body/a22454409/body-fat-different-types/

19 'The Schofield Equation', YMCA fit, https://elearning.ymca.co.uk/pluginfile.php/20660/mod_resource/content/1/The%20Schofield%20Equation.pdf; There is an interactive site where you can find out your own rates at: Schofield Equation Basal Metabolic Rate, Global RPh, https://globalrph.com/medcalcs/schofield-equation-bmr/

20 International Agency for Research on Cancer (World Health Organisation), *Q & A on the carcinogenicity of the consumption of red meat and processed meat*, http://www.iarc.fr/en/media-centre/iarcnews/pdf/Monographs-Q&A_Vol114.pdf

21 Jana J Anderson et al, 'Red and processed meat consumption and breast

cancer: UK Biobank cohort study and meta-analysis', *European Journal of Cancer*, February 2018, volume 90, pp. 73–82 www.ejcancer.com/article/S0959-8049(17)31430-2/fulltext

22 Alexandra Richards, 'Sausages and Bacon "increase breast cancer risk" in older women, study reveals', *Evening Standard*, 4 January 2018

23 Giuseppe Faraco et al, 'Dietary salt promotes neurovascular and cognitive dysfunction through a gut-initiated TH17 response', *Nature Neuroscience*, 2018, pp. 240 ff, https://www.nature.com/articles/s41593-017-0059-z.epdf?referrer_access_token=KzT0r5uRQM05ivlFSlibI9RgN0jAjWel9jnR3ZoTvOOTWb3ivyND78Ad-xKgJSwDit2ARKK5MSVkSrVtY1istUs52OEvWtYzUjLB6IgDlRP_bGSwVbP16YyJ4ppvnDDDiOPqi61DlgdAzJyQy8mFQvGz9PJ3b910Wp-MYYtazMPVqqbrcAqPUJMmb70QvPGw5KUqc9aKnLQflwtCa0ZEpkAnVjmVRFeuJ8pFr_hwQ6SUmDQ5wDcrxdK3ROOcJhKQZcjS35rWqLbpHh7ez2erPB_mkUbrXWW766dFdQmLCF0%3D&tracking_referrer=www.genengnews.com

24 C Carnell et al, 'Morning and afternoon appetite and gut hormone responses to meal and stress challenges in obese individuals with and without binge eating disorder', *International Journal of Obesity*, 13 December 2017, https://www.nature.com/articles/ijo2017307

25 'One in six young people eat fast food "twice a day"', *BBC News*, 30 September 2016 http://www.bbc.co.uk/news/health-37511554

26 Prakash Deedwania and Tushar Achcryer, 'Hearty Breakfast for Healthier Arteries', *Journal of the American College of Cardiology*, 70 (15), October 2017, http://www.onlinejacc.org/content/70/15/1843?sso=1&sso_redirect_count=1&access_token=

27 'Can muesli help against arthritis?' University of Friedrich-Alexander-Universtät Erlangen-Nürmberg, 12 January 2018, https://www.fau.eu/2018/01/12/news/research/can-muesli-help-against-arthritis/

28 Francesca Rice, 'Eat this one thing for breakfast to help ward off arthritis, says scientists', *Prima*, 15 January 2018 http://www.prima.co.uk/diet-and-health/healthy-living/news/a42184/muesli-breakfast-arthritis/

29 Cited in Henry Bodkin, 'A single yoghurt can max-out children's daily sugar allowance', *Daily Telegraph*, 23 April 2018, https://www.telegraph.co.uk/news/2018/04/23/single-yoghurt-can-max-out-childrens-daily-

sugar-allowance-officials/

30 For more information, see '6 ways to practice mindful eating', *Mindful*, https://www.mindful.org/6-ways-practice-mindful-eating/

31 Emma Gray, 'Slow eating speed may be linked to weight loss', *BMJ Open*, 12 February 2018, http://blogs.bmj.com/bmjopen/2018/02/12/slow-eating-speed-may-be-linked-to-weight-loss/

32 He defines happiness as opposed to pleasure in the following terms: 'Pleasure is short-lived, happiness is long-lived; pleasure is visceral, happiness is ethereal; pleasure is taking, happiness is giving; pleasure can be achieved with substances, happiness cannot be achieved with substances; and, finally, pleasure is experienced alone, happiness is usually experienced in social groups.' Quoted in: Erin Bunch, 'Pleasure is making you miserable—here's how to find true happiness instead', 26 September 2017, https://wellandgood.com/good-advice/difference-between-pleasure-happiness/

33 Cited in: Erin Bunch, 'Pleasure is making you miserable—here's how to find true happiness instead', 26 September 2017, https://wellandgood.com/good-advice/difference-between-pleasure-happiness/

34 Vanessa Garcia-Larsen et al, 'Dietary antioxidants and 10-year lung function decline in adults from the ECRHS survey', *European Respiratory Journal*, 50 (6), December 2017, http://erj.ersjournals.com/content/50/6/1602286

35 K L Stanhope et al, 'Pathways and mechanisms linking dietary components to cardiometabolic disease: thinking beyond calories', *Obesity Reviews*, 2018, https://onlinelibrary.wiley.com/doi/epdf/10.1111/obr.12699

36 Quoted in: Rachel Hosie, 'Why you should never go on another diet', *The Independent*, 23 February 2018, https://www.independent.co.uk/life-style/health-and-families/dieting-why-bad-weight-watchers-loss-diets-healthy-lifestyle-a8219636.html

37 Yolanda Zaw, 'The simple trick to help you lose weight that isn't about food or exercise', 4 June 2018, https://evoke.ie/2018/06/04/fit/motivation/trick-to-lose-weight-and-keep-it-off-that-isnt-about-food-or-fitness

38 Roy J Hardman et al, 'Adherence to a Mediterranean Style Diet and Effects on Cognition in Adults: A Qualitative Evaluation and Systematic Review of Longitudinal and Prospective Trials', *Frontiers in Nutrition*, 22 July 2016, https://www.frontiersin.org/articles/10.3389/fnut.2016.00022/full

8 Healthy drinking

> That everyone may eat and drink, and find satisfaction in all his toil—this is the gift of God (Ecclesiastes 3:13).

The way to confront obesity is more than eating the right food and undertaking the appropriate amount of exercise. Obesity is also caused by the added consumption of high-calorie soft and alcoholic drinks—many of which have a high sugar content.

For example, where there is a great increase in the intake of alcohol, it results in swelling bellies and it wreaks havoc on our bodies. Indeed, the term 'beer belly' has become part of our vocabulary.

Stress

It has been estimated that three in five adults who drink alcohol do so in order to cope with the stresses of daily life. A survey of 18- to 75-year-olds in the United Kingdom discovered that 38 per cent of those who had drunk alcohol in the previous twelve months had done so to forget their problems for at least some of the time.

Nearly half of them had drunk alcohol to bring them into a better mood, whereas 58 per cent had drunk to forget the normal stresses of everyday living.

The survey had also found that 41 per cent had drunk because they felt depressed or nervous.

The findings were equal for men and women, and generally across all of the age ranges.

The higher rate was to be observed among the lower social grades as they drank to alleviate their worries about financial and housing concerns.

Elaine Hindal, the Drinkaware chief executive, commented:

> Whilst people might think having a drink after a hard day can help them relax, in the long run it can contribute to feelings of depression and anxiety and make stress harder to deal with.
>
> This is because regular, heavy drinking interferes with the neurotransmitters in our brains that are needed for good mental health.

She continued to point out that regular drinking lowers the levels of serotonin (the chemical in the brain that regulates moods) which can lead to a downward spiral of depression.[1]

Happiness is short lived because alcohol is a depressant; it lowers the levels of serotonin, the hormone that produces happiness. Serotonin is a neurotransmitter that enables you to keep calm and happy. However, low levels of the hormone results in increased anxiety.

As a person's body becomes tolerant to alcohol, drinking will become less effective in causing relaxation. The net result is that increasing amounts of alcohol will need to be consumed in order to get the original sense of ease, so it becomes a vicious cycle.

Cancer

Excess alcohol can damage the liver, resulting in pancreatitis (the inflammation of the pancreas) and is responsible for the development of seven types of cancer, according to Cancer Research

UK. Indeed, alcohol is responsible for over 12,000 cancer referrals annually in the United Kingdom.

Alcohol damages the DNA blueprint in stem cells, which could be the cause of the cancers.[2] The process involves a toxic chemical called acetaldehyde being produced in the liver when alcohol is broken down, which then breaks down and damages the DNA within blood stem cells. It alters the sequences irreversibly while rearranging irreparably the whole DNA strand or individual chromosomes.[3]

Alcohol can cause 7 types of cancer (according to Cancer Research UK) In the order of the number of cancer cases that occur:
Bowel
Breast (in women)
Mouth
Oesophagus
Larynx
Liver
Upper Throat

Benefits of abstinence

Research has discovered that people who abstained in 'Dry January' had enormous health benefits, which had a lasting impact one month onwards.

In the following August, they were still consuming less alcohol, with their drinking days having dropped from 4.3 to 3.3 days a week. They were also drinking less quantities as, on their drinking days, the units fell from 8.6 to 7.1 on average. The frequency of being drunk also dropped from 3.4 times a month to 2.1 times.

It was also revealed that 70 per cent commented on their health having improved as a result of their reduced drinking, with 71 per cent having better sleep and 67 per cent reporting to have improved energy.

Weight had been lost by 58 per cent of the respondents and better skin was experienced by 54 per cent.

There were also emotional positives as 93 per cent felt a sense of achievement and 53 per cent had better concentration.

In addition, there were changes in their attitudes towards alcohol with 71 per cent realising that they did not need to drink in order to enjoy themselves and 80 per cent feeling more in control of their drinking by the end of the month. Eighty-two per cent had thought more deeply about their relationship with alcohol, and 76 per cent felt more educated about when and why they drank.

On the practical side, 93 per cent felt a sense of achievement in participating in 'Dry January', while 88 per cent had saved money.[4]

Effects on obesity

Alcohol has an effect on weight as it is full of carbohydrates and has a high sugar content. In addition to the ill effects mentioned previously in this chapter, the immoderate use of alcohol will also contribute to the general effects of obesity.

When we are seeking to live how God wants us to, we need to reduce or even eliminate alcohol consumption so that we can monitor our weight.

ACTION POINTS

- *Change to drinking low sugar and low alcohol/no alcohol*

alternatives (although drinking a large amount of low-sugar drinks with artificial sweeteners in is not healthy either. Water is the best!).

- *Try abstaining from alcohol completely during 'Dry January' or a month of your choice.*

NOTES

1 Cited in Eleanor Rose, 'Majority of drinkers do it to cope with stresses of everyday life, survey finds', *Evening Standard,* 16 January 2018, https://www.standard.co.uk/news/uk/majority-of-drinkers-do-it-to-cope-with-stresses-of-everyday-life-survey-finds-a3739911.html

2 Natasha Hinde, 'Just One in 10 People know alcohol can cause cancer, survey reveals', *Huffington Post UK*, 8 January 2017, https://www.huffingtonpost.co.uk/entry/one-in-10-people-know-alcohol-can-cause-cancer-survey-reveals_uk_5a533eabe4b0efe47eba37b4?guccounter=1

3 MRC (Medical Research Council) Laboratory of Molecular Biology, Cambridge, 'New research shows how alcohol damages DNA, which may increase cancer risk', 3 January 2018, https://mrc.ukri.org/news/browse/new-research-shows-how-alcohol-damages-dna-which-may-increase-cancer-risk/

4 Anna Ford, 'How "Dry January" is the secret to better sleep, saving money and losing weight', *University of Sussex*, 2 January 2019, http://www.sussex.ac.uk/broadcast/read/47131http://www.sussex.ac.uk/broadcast/read/47131

9 Fasting

I turned to the LORD God and pleaded with him in prayer and petition, in fasting (Daniel 9:3).

Fasting is an integral part of a book, written from the biblical perspective, on obesity and being overweight. It is a neglected spiritual discipline that I can put up my hands, in common with other Christians, to acknowledge that I am not very good at it.

While fasting does have powerful spiritual implications, it has physical benefits as well. It is not surprising, as God created us as holistic beings and so fasting will inevitably cause us to profit, not only in our spirits and souls, but also in our bodies. In fasting, we are involving each part of our being—spirit, mind and body.

We often emphasise, rightly, that Jesus fasted in order to commune closely with His Father. However, in doing this, we do neglect the fact that the act of fasting also sharpened His mind and strengthened His body for the work that He was to do.

In fasting, we realise that we are not infinite. In the most surprising of quotes, the atheist Friedrich Nietzsche commented: 'The belly is the reason why man does not so readily take himself for a god.'[1]

However impressive the endorsement of man is, we have to remember that the Bible was there first. The Hebrew word 'to fast' is tsoom, which literally means to abstain from food. The comparable word in the Greek is nēsteuō, which has the added nuance of meaning 'to be empty'. In other words, we are not only to be emptied of food but also of those things that entrap us and keep us away from God.

The nature of fasting is the abstinence from all or some food stuffs or drinks for a set period of time. In general terms, as we can see, the majority of fasts are 24 to 72 hours in duration.

Alternatively, we can undertake intermittent fasting which involves oscillating between periods of eating and fasting, from a few hours to a few days at a time.

It means that you do not have to undertake constant fasting but can pick the one that is most suitable for you in your circumstances. It will be prudent not to fast if you have a medical condition that precludes it (such as gastrointestinal, cardiac or Type 1 diabetes) or are pregnant/just given birth. In situations where you are unsure, it is always best to seek medical advice.

There are various types of fasting including:

- The Warrior Diet where you fast during the day (eating only raw fruits and vegetables) and have a big meal at night in a four-hour window (excluding processed foods but emphasising plenty of fresh produce).
- 5:2 diet (where you eat normally for five days and fast on the other two, reducing the calories to 500 to 600 calories).
- The 'Eat-Stop-Eat' method, which is similar to the 5:2 method except that a person does not eat at all for a 24-hour period once or twice a week although water, coffee and non-calorific drinks are allowed.
- A more popular version called 16:8 diet (also known as a Leangains), where eating is restricted to an eight-hour window so you are effectively fasting for 16 hours a day.

- Alternate Day Fast (also known as ADF, where you fast every other day). It could be as simple as fasting for a day where your calorie intake is limited to 500 calories a day, missing a meal or simply abandoning the idea of that usual snack. Very often, we think that we are hungry when, in fact, we are requiring a drink to satisfy our appetite—a mistake that 73 per cent of us make.[2]

However, it is not to be a discipline that we are to show off in front of others. Indeed, Jesus warned us that it was a private matter between us and God:

> When you fast, do not look sombre as the hypocrites do, for they disfigure their faces to show men they are fasting. I tell you the truth, they have received their reward in full. But when you fast, put oil on your head and wash your face, so that it will not be obvious to men that you are fasting, but only to your Father, who is unseen; and your Father, who sees what is done in secret, will reward you (Matthew 6:16–18).

It is an attitude that permeated the Church in the early days as the Venerable Thalassius the Libyan (died c. 660) stated: 'To fast well is to enjoy simple food in small amounts and to shun other people's esteem.'[3]

The practice has continued as Orthodox Christians make it a discipline to fast before Easter in the season of Lent. However, they also fast in 'little Lent' in preparation for Advent. It is telling that these are the two seasons when many Christians consume the most.

Spiritual

The primary reason for fasting is to come into a closer relationship with God.

It could be expressed in one of the following purposes:[4]

TO SHOW SORROW FOR SIN, WHETHER PERSONAL OR NATIONAL. EXAMPLES:

- Daniel 9:3: 'So I turned to the LORD God and pleaded with Him in prayer and petition, in fasting, and in sackcloth and ashes.'
- Ezra 10:6: 'Then Ezra withdrew from before the house of God … he ate no food and drank no water, because he continued to mourn over the unfaithfulness of the exiles.'
- Nehemiah 1:4: 'When I heard these things, I sat down and wept. For some days I mourned and fasted and prayed before the God of heaven.'
- Jonah 3:5, 10: 'The Ninevites believed God. They declared a fast, and all of them, from the greatest to the least, put on sackcloth … When God saw what they did and how they turned from their evil ways, he had compassion and did not bring upon them the destruction he had threatened.'

TO BE HUMBLE BEFORE GOD
EXAMPLES:

- 1 Kings 21:27–29: 'When Ahab heard these words, he tore his clothes, put on sackcloth and fasted. He lay in sackcloth and went around meekly. Then the word of the LORD came to Elijah the Tishbite: "Have you noticed how Ahab has humbled himself before me? Because he has humbled himself, I will not bring this disaster in his day, but I will bring it on his house in the days of his son".'
- Psalm 35:13: '… I put on sackcloth and humbled myself with fasting.'

TO HEAR FROM GOD AND/OR SEEK HIS INTERVENTION
EXAMPLES:

- Esther 4:16: 'Do not eat or drink for three days, night or day. I and my maids will fast as you do. When this is done, I will go to the king, even though it is against the law. And if I perish, I perish.'
- Ezra 8:21, 23: 'There, by the Ahava Canal, I proclaimed a fast, so that we might humble ourselves before our God and ask him for a safe journey for us and our children with all our possessions ... So, we fasted and petitioned our God about this, and he answered our prayer.'

TO STRENGTHEN PRAYER
EXAMPLES:

- Ezra 8:23: 'So we fasted and petitioned our God about this, and he answered our prayer.'
- Joel 2:12: '"Even now," declares the Lord, "return to me with all your heart, with fasting and weeping, and mourning".'
- Acts 13:3: 'So after they had fasted and prayed, they placed their hands on them and sent them off.'

TO EXPRESS GRIEF
EXAMPLES:

- 1 Samuel 31:13: 'Then they took their bones and buried them under a tamarisk tree at Jabesh, and they fasted seven days.'
- 2 Samuel 1:11–12: 'Then David and all the men with him ... mourned and wept and fasted till evening for Saul and his son Jonathan, and for the army of the Lord and the house of Israel, because they had fallen by the sword.'

**TO SEEK DISCERNMENT FOR AN UPCOMING DECISION OR
GUIDANCE FOR NEXT STEPS
EXAMPLES:**

- Judges 20:26: 'Then the Israelites, all the people, went up to Bethel, and there they sat weeping before the LORD. They fasted that day until evening and presented burnt offerings and fellowship offerings to the LORD.'
- Acts 9:9: 'For three days he was blind, and did not eat or drink anything.'
- Acts 13:1–3, especially v. 2: 'While they were worshipping the Lord and fasting, the Holy Spirit said ...'
- Acts 14:23: 'Paul and Barnabas appointed elders for them in each church and, with prayer and fasting, committed them to the Lord, in whom they had put their trust.'

**TO EXPRESS CONCERN FOR THE WORK OF GOD
EXAMPLES:**

- Nehemiah 1:4: 'When I heard these things, I sat down and wept. For some days I mourned and fasted and prayed before the God of heaven.'
- Daniel 9: 3: 'So I turned to the LORD God and pleaded with him in prayer and petition, in fasting, and in sackcloth and ashes.'

**TO OVERCOME TEMPTATION AND TO DEDICATE YOURSELF TO GOD
EXAMPLE:**

- Matthew 4:1–11: Before Jesus was tempted, He fasted for forty days and forty nights (v. 2).

These very areas overlap with the subject matters covered elsewhere in this book. As an example, it could be that you are wanting to be involved with environmental aspects as you are concerned about what we are doing to God's creation and turning what was good into something bad. You might then require guidance as to what you should do next.

Alternatively, your goal might be to eat less so self-control will be a priority—you do not need guidance not to overindulge as God has already said that it is a sin. It is like asking for guidance not to rob a bank or look at pornographic material—God has already spoken on these matters. What might help is godly guidance as to support groups or a person that you can be honest with and be held accountable in the areas of monitoring your weight, eating healthily and exercising well. It has to be remembered that others, however great their concern for you, will not always be there to police your calorie intake.

There has to be recognition that letting go of what we see around us, including what is in our fridge or larder, will concentrate our hearts and minds on what God wants from us, for us and through us. Andrew Murray has stated: 'Prayer is reaching out after the unseen; fasting is letting go of all that is seen and temporal. Fasting helps express, deepen, confirm the resolution that we are ready to sacrifice anything, even ourselves to attain what we seek for the kingdom of God.'[5]

More recently, Rowan Williams, the former Archbishop of Canterbury, has described fasting as 'denying yourself the pleasures of thinking of yourself as an isolated being with no real relations with those around; denying yourself the fantasy that you can organise the world to suit yourself; denying yourself the luxury of not noticing the suffering of your neighbour.'[6]

The process of fasting can take many forms, not only in the temporary and voluntary withdrawal from food, but also from other activities (such as technology) so that we turn from worshipping and concentrating on God's good gifts and turn to placing our whole beings on God Himself.

It could include restricting our travel to the basics (such as going to work or school) and not journeying to our favourite coffee shop or delicatessen so that we can indulge in our luxuries. Dr Martyn Lloyd-Jones has summarised it in these words: 'Fasting, if we conceive of it truly, must not be confined to the question of food and drink; fasting should really be made to include abstinence from anything which is legitimate in and of itself for the sake of some special spiritual purpose. There are many bodily functions which are right and normal and perfectly legitimate, but which, for special peculiar reasons, should be controlled. That is fasting.'[7]

John Piper has expanded the boundaries of our concepts of fasting further: 'Rising early is a kind of fast. A coming to pray when it is hard to get there is another kind of fast. When we make such choices, we make war on the deceitfulness of our desires and declare the preciousness of prayer and the all-surpassing worth of God.'[8]

However, despite this widening of the boundary of meaning, we have to acknowledge that fasting is showing primarily that we think our relationship with God is more important than the food that we eat. It is often the case that we get our priorities wrong and think that the world, or (in our heights of self-aggrandisement) God, owes us one.

We sit comfortably in Bible study groups and quote the works of the Puritans and others without realising the cost that they had to face. If we had to encounter the fasting (both voluntary and involuntary) that they thought of as godly disciplines then we can identify with the spiritual maturity that comes through fasting—both the removal or reduction of food, or the absence of other material comforts. We have come to acquire a mentality that the heights of relationship that those in the past had with God can be obtained by us taking the easy routes of 'cheap grace' (as Dietrich Bonhoeffer termed it), whereas God wants us to demonstrate that we are serious in approaching Him.

The number of effective servants for God's Kingdom is incalculable in the past, for they were willing to give up everything—to be lean spiritually as well as physically. If our fellowships are full of people who are obese, there is the danger that we can become flabby spiritually also. We need to be physically and spiritually fit for gospel work.

When we have flexed our fingers away from the food in front of us and looked to the Giver, we will then be on the right track. As Paul told of his own experiences: 'I am not saying this because I am in need, for I have learned to be content whatever the circumstances. I know what it is to be in need, and I know what it is to have plenty. I have learned the secret of being content in any and every situation, whether well fed or hungry, whether living in plenty or in want. I can do everything through him who gives me strength' (Philippians 4:11–13).

It is this other-world awareness that makes us fit to do God's will in this world because we are open to His transforming of our minds (Romans 12:2). Dietrich Bonhoeffer was a German Pastor who was executed by the Nazis in World War II because he chose to follow

Jesus. He was a person willing to forgo the material benefits of this world for the progression of the kingdom of God and stated: 'Jesus takes it for granted that his disciples will observe the pious custom of fasting. Strict exercise of self-control is an essential feature of the Christian's life. Such customs have only one purpose—to make the disciples more ready and cheerful to accomplish those things which God would have done.'[9]

Fasting is not a practice for the ascetics or 'super holy'; it is meant to be the normal practice of Bible-believing Christians—as though there were any other alternatives! It is as though we want a short cut to sanctification without the lessons that God wants to teach us. There is no lazy way to knowing God as He wants to draw close to us without other things, such as our unhealthy obsession on food, getting in the way.

C S Lewis adds: 'It is impossible to accept Christianity for the sake of finding comfort; but the Christian tries to lay himself open to the will of God, to do what God wants him to do. You don't know in advance whether God is going to set you to do something difficult or painful, or something that you will quite like; and some people of heroic mould are disappointed when the job doled out to them turns out to be something quite nice. But you must be prepared for the unpleasant things and the discomforts. I don't mean fasting, and things like that. They are a different matter. When you are training soldiers in manoeuvres, you practise in blank ammunition because you would like them to have practices before meeting the real enemy. So, we must abstain from pleasures which are not in themselves wicked. If you don't abstain from pleasure, you won't be good when the time comes along. It is purely a matter of practice.'[10]

Physical

God has made us as holistic people. He created us to be as one, not to be divided artificially into body, mind and spirit. As He commands us to fast, in order that we can get our spiritual priorities in order, He also knows that it will benefit our bodies.

INTERMITTENT FASTING ALTERS THE FUNCTIONS OF CELLS, GENES AND HORMONES

When the body does not receive food for a while, there are important cellular repair processes and changes in the hormone levels to make stored fat more available to burn.

Dr J H Tilden confessed: 'After fifty-five years of sojourning in the wilderness of medical therapeutics, I am forced to declare ... that fasting is the only reliable, specific, therapeutic eliminant known to man.'[11]

The changes include the following:

Insulin levels

The blood levels of insulin decline rapidly, which aids in the burning of fat.[12] The purpose of lowering the insulin resistance is to increase the body's sensitivity to insulin, which enables it to transport glucose from the blood to the cells more effectively and prevents the build-up of blood sugar levels. The blood sugar levels will remain constantly steady, without the dramatic ups and downs, eliminating the need to reach out for the sugary treats.

The increase in insulin production will assist in the lowering of blood sugar levels and so prevent the occurrence of Type 2 diabetes, often to a spectacular effect.[13] It was shown that fasting reduces blood sugar by 3 to 6 per cent, while insulin resistance was reduced by 20 to 31 per cent. The result was that it was more effective than limiting calorie intake, so it also had the added benefit of controlling weight.

People who have Type 2 diabetes, or are likely to develop it, and undertake short-term intermittent fasts are more likely to experience significantly lower blood sugar levels.

Intermittent fasting could protect against kidney damage, which is one of the more devastating effects of diabetes.

The proviso is that there may be some differences between the genders, as one study indicated that blood sugar control worsened in nonobese women after a 22-day-long intermittent fasting programme.[14]

Human growth hormone (HGH)

The blood levels of growth hormone may increase as much as five times.[15] The higher levels of this key hormone will be instrumental in the burning of fat and gain in muscle, together with many other benefits such as metabolism and weight loss.[16]

There have been several pieces of research that discovered fasting might increase HGH levels naturally. It has been shown that fasting for 24 hours would increase the levels of HGH significantly.[17]

Norepinephrine will be increased

This hormone deals with stress and is also a neurotransmitter (it sends signals between the nerve cells). Its increase will facilitate the breakdown of body fat so it can be used for energy.

Cellular repair

Fasting enables important cellular repair processes, such as removing waste material from cells, called autophagy.[18]

It involves the cells breaking down and metabolising broken and dysfunctional proteins that build up inside cells over time. A result will be that wounds will heal quicker as the old dead cells will be replaced quicker. It is also true as far as acne is concerned as the cells will be replaced by healthier ones.

This increased autophagy, or cleansing process, may give added protection against a number of diseases, including cancer and Alzheimer's Disease.[19]

Incidentally, intermittent fasting may not only prevent the occurrence of cancer, but there is also some proof that this practice may reduce the various side effects of chemotherapy for cancer patients.[20]

Dr Joel Fuhrman has stated: 'The body's wonderous ability to self-digest and destroy needless tissues such as fat, blood vessel plaque, and other nonessential and diseased tissues, while conserving essential tissues, gives the fast the ability to restore ... youth to the system.'[21]

Gene expression
Going without food on a temporary basis is beneficial for several genes and molecules that are instrumental in longevity of life and protection against disease.[22]

Reduces oxidative stress and inflammation in the body
Oxidative stress is one of the progressive steps towards ageing and many chronic diseases.[23] This stress involves free radicals, which are unstable molecules that interact with other important molecules (such as protein and DNA) and damage them.[24]

The good news is that it has been demonstrated that intermittent fasting could actually strengthen the body's resistance to oxidative stress.[25] It is not only the importance of eating antioxidants (such as blueberries, oranges, grapes and kale), but the proactive action of fasting that helps the body in this way.

In addition, there have been studies that demonstrate intermittent fasting being able to assist in combatting inflammation—one of the key components of many common diseases (such as heart disease, cancer and rheumatoid arthritis)— especially as the body ages. One study found that intermittent fasting for one month assisted in decreasing inflammation levels. Another study found that when people fasted for 12 hours a day for one month, it was beneficial in dealing with both inflammation and reducing asthma. [26]

HEART BENEFITS

Heart disease is the world's biggest killer, but intermittent fasting has been proved to reduce the risk factors that cause it. The reduced risk factors include the following: blood pressure, total and LDL cholesterol, blood triglycerides, inflammatory markers and blood sugar levels.[27]

Eight weeks of alternate-day fasting can reduce 'bad' LDL cholesterol and blood triglycerides by 25 per cent and 32 per cent, respectively.[28]

There is also a link between fasting and a lower risk of coronary artery disease, as well as a markedly lower risk of diabetes, which is an important risk factor for heart disease.[29]

WEIGHT LOSS

There are always those who are fasting in order to lose weight as part of a calorie-controlled diet.[30] As part of this regime, it is the reduction in the number of meals with the same size of servings (not larger). If the other meals compensate by having more on the plate, then the result will be more calories converted to fat in your body.

It is estimated that the body burns approximately 1750 calories a day. By contrast, with intermittent fasting, the body will be burning an addition of approximately 3600 calories per week, which is the equivalent of one pound every week.

The lower insulin levels, high growth hormone levels and the increase in norepinephrine all contribute to the increased metabolic rate by 3.6 to 14 per cent, which in turn will result in more calories being burned.[31]

Indeed, it is a win-win situation as the metabolic rate is increased (so calories are expelled) and the consumption of food is reduced (so the number of calories present is diminished).

It was calculated that intermittent fasting can result in a weight loss of 3 to 8 per cent over 3 to 24 weeks. People can reduce their waist circumference by 4 to 7 per cent, indicating that they lost fat in the abdominal cavity (which is responsible for diseases and conditions such as Type 2 diabetes).[32]

Another review showed that fasting for a whole day could reduce body weight by up to 9 per cent and could decrease body fat significantly over a 12-to-24-week period.[33]

In addition, intermittent fasting leads to less muscle loss than continuous calorie restriction, for intermittent fasting over 3 to 12 weeks is as effective in losing weight as continuous calorie restriction, while reducing body weight by 8 per cent and fat mass by 16 per cent.[34]

Mental

There is proof that intermittent fasting, such as the 5:2 diet, could improve memory and learning capabilities. The process is certainly assisted by the reduced oxidative stress, reduced inflammation and the reduction in blood sugar levels and insulin resistance.

As a result of fasting, neurons are given more energy which enables them to develop more connections. It is caused by a 50 per cent increase in the brain chemical BDNF (brain-derived neurotrophic factor), which promotes the growth of nerve cells and improves overall cognitive functioning. A deficiency in this brain chemical has been implicated in depression and other neurological problems.[35]

In the times of intermittent fasting, the body changes energy sources from glucose, originating in the liver, to fat cells which stimulate activity and growth in the brain.

There were signs that there is increased alertness and more activity in the areas of the brain responsible for learning and memory during the fasting period. There is also the benefit that the nerve growth from protein reduces the impact of diseases such as Alzheimer's, Parkinson's and Huntingdon's.[36]

It will assist in remembering (such as Bible verses) and in reasoning, so extending our ability to serve God and other people. However, it is does not reverse the ageing process where our mental capacity is naturally reduced, but it does mean that we can stave off those days and not hasten their arrival.

Fasting matters

We have seen in this chapter that fasting is not only beneficial for our physical and mental health; it also sharpens us spiritually.

We need churches full of people who are fit in all aspects of their lives in order to serve God, which can only come about by fasting and prayer.

ACTION POINTS

- *Undertake a fast if you are physically able to do so.*
- *Think about the reasons why you are fasting.*
- *Rely on God, especially at this time, as it is one of those occasions when you are liable to be tempted by the devil.*

NOTES

1 Friedrich Nietzsche, 'Chapter IV, Apophthegms and Interlude', *Beyond Good and Evil*, Point 141, translated by Helen Zimmern, https://en.wikisource.org/wiki/Beyond_Good_and_Evil/Chapter_IV

2 PKD Foundation, *Hunger vs. thirst: tips to tell the difference*, https://pkdcure.org/blog/hunger-vs-thirs

3 https://livingmaronite.files.wordpress.com/2017/02/fasting-for-strength.pdf

4 See, for example, Len Woods, *Rose Guide to Discipleship* (Rose Publishing, 2019) and Don Whitney, *Spiritual Disciplines* (Colorado Springs: NavPress, 2014)

5 https://www.beliefnet.com/quotes/evangelical/a/andrew-murray/prayer-is-reaching-out-after-the-unseen-fasting-i.asp

6 'Dr Williams begins a tour of India', *The Church of England Newspaper*, 15 October 2010, p. 7

7 Martyn Lloyd-Jones, *Studies in the Sermon on the Mount*, volume 2 (Leicester: Inter Varsity Press, 2000), p. 38

8   John Piper, *A Hunger for God* (Wheaton, Illinois: Crossway, 1997), p. 48

9   Dietrich Bonhoeffer, *The Cost of Discipleship* (London: SCM Press, 2001), p. 188

10 C S Lewis, 'Answers to Questions on Christianity', *God in the Dock* (Grand Rapids, Michigan: Eerdmans, 1970), pp. 53–54

11 Shane Idleman, 'Fasting Health: The Physical Affects the Spiritual', *Christian Headlines*, 4 January 2019, https://www.christianheadlines.com/columnists/guest-commentary/fasting-health-the-physical-affects-the-spiritual.html

12 L K Heilbronn, SR Smith, CK Martin, S D Anton and E Ravussin, 'Alternate-day fasting in nonobese subjects: effects on body weight, body composition, and energy metabolism', *American Journal of Clinical Nutrition*, January 2005, 81 (1), pp. 69–73, https://www.ncbi.nlm.nih.gov/pubmed/15640462

13 Adrienne R Barnosky, Kristin K Hoddy, Terry G Unterman and Krista A Varady, 'Intermittent fasting vs daily calorie restriction for type 2 diabetes prevention: a review of human findings', *Translational Research*, October 2014, 164 (4), pp. 302–311, https://www.sciencedirect.com/science/article/pii/S193152441400200X

14 LK Heilbronn et al, 'Glucose tolerance and skeletal muscle gene expression in response to alternate day fasting', *Obesity Review*, March 2005, 13 (3), 574–81, https://onlinelibrary.wiley.com/doi/full/10.1038/oby.2005.61

15 See, for example, ABW Tavares et al, 'Effects of Growth Hormone Administration on Muscle Strength in Men over 50 Years Old', *International Journal of Endocrinology*, 8 December 2013, https://www.ncbi.nlm.nih.gov/pmc/articles/PMC3870652/pdf/IJE2013-942030.pdf

16 MR Blackman et al, 'Growth hormone and sex steroid administration in healthy aged women and men: a randomised controlled trial', *Journal of American Medical Association*, November 2002, 288 (18), 2282–92, https://www.ncbi.nlm.nih.gov/pubmed/12425705

17 B Salgin et al, 'The effect of prolonged fasting on levels of growth hormone-binding protein and free growth hormone', *Growth Hormone & IGF Research*, April 2012, 22 (2), 76–81, https://www.sciencedirect.com/

science/article/pii/S1096637412000184?via%3Dihub

18   Mehrdad Alirezael et al, 'Short-term fasting induces profound neuronal autophagy', *Autophagy*, 16 August 2010, 6 (6), 702–710, https://www.ncbi.nlm.nih.gov/pmc/articles/PMC3106288/ ; I Kim and JJ Lemasters, 'Mitochondrial degradation by autophagy (mitophagy) in GFP-LC3 transgenic hepatocytes during nutrient deprivation', *American Journal of Physiology Cell Physiology*, February 2011, 200 (2), C 308–17, https://www.ncbi.nlm.nih.gov/pmc/articles/PMC30436

19   DM Wolfe et al, 'Autophagy failure in Alzheimer's disease and the role of defective lysosomal acidification', *European Journal of Neuroscience*, June 2013, 37 (12), 1949–61, https://www.ncbi.nlm.nih.gov/pmc/articles/PMC3694736/

20   FM Safdie et al, 'Fasting and cancer treatment in humans: A case series report', *Aging (Albany, NY)*, 31 December 2009, 1 (12), 988–1007, https://www.ncbi.nlm.nih.gov/pmc/articles/PMC2815756/

21   Shane Idleman, 'Fasting Health: The Physical Affects the Spiritual', *Christian Headlines*, 4 January 2019, https://www.christianheadlines.com/columnists/guest-commentary/fasting-health-the-physical-affects-the-spiritual.html

22   Y Zhu, Y Yan, GR Gius and A Vassilopoulos, 'Metabolic regulation of Sirtuins upon fasting and the implication for cancer', *Current Opinion in Oncology*, November 2013, 25 (6), 630–6, https://www.ncbi.nlm.nih.gov/pmc/articles/PMC5525320/

23   R De Bont and N van Larebeke, 'Endogenous DNA damage in humans: a review of quantitative data', *Mutagenesis*, May 2004, 19 (3), 169–85, https://www.ncbi.nlm.nih.gov/pubmed/15123782

24   Anu Rahal et al, 'Oxidative Stress, Prooxidants, and Antioxidants: The Interplay', *BioMed Research International*, volume 2014, Article ID 761264, https://www.hindawi.com/journals/bmri/2014/761264/

25   Mark P Mattson and Ruiquin Wan, 'Beneficial effects of intermittent fasting and calorific restriction on the cardiovascular and cerebrovascular systems', *Journal of Nutritional Biochemistry,* 16 (3), 129–137, https://www.sciencedirect.com/science/article/pii/S095528630400261X

26   See, for example, Philip Hunter, 'The inflammation theory of disease',

EMBO Reports, November 2012, 13 (11), 968–970, https://www.ncbi.nlm.nih.gov/pmc/articles/PMC3492709/

27 Adrienne R Barnosky et al, 'Intermittent fasting vs daily calorie restriction for type 2 diabetes prevention: a review of human findings', *Translational Research*, October 2014, 164 (4), 302–311, https://www.sciencedirect.com/science/article/pii/S193152441400200X

28 S Bhutani, MC Klempel, RA Berger and KS Varady, 'Improvements in coronary heart disease risk indicators by alternate-day fasting involve adipose tissue modulations', *Obesity (Silver Spring)*, November 2010, 18 (11), 2152–9, https://onlinelibrary.wiley.com/doi/full/10.1038/oby.2010.54

29 Benjamin D Horne et al, 'Usefulness of Routine Periodic Fasting to Lower Risk of Coronary Artery Disease among Patients Undergoing Coronary Angiography', *American Journal of Cardiology*, 1 October 2008, 102 (7), 814–819, https://www.ajconline.org/article/S0002-9149(08)00901-6/fulltext

30 A Johnstone, 'Fasting for weight loss: an effective strategy or latest dieting trend?' *International Journal of Obesity*, 26 December 2014, 39 (5), 727–33, https://www.nature.com/articles/ijo2014214

31 C Zauner et al, 'Resting energy expenditure in short-term starvation is increased as a result of an increase in serum norepinephrine', *American Journal of Clinical Nutrition*, June 2000, 71 (6), 1511–5, https://academic.oup.com/ajcn/article/71/6/1511/4

32 Adrienne R Barnosky et al, 'Intermittent fasting vs daily calorie restriction for type 2 diabetes prevention: a review of human findings', *Translational Research*, October 2014, 164 (4), 302–311, https://www.sciencedirect.com/science/article/pii/S193152441400200X

33 GM Tinsley and PM La Bounty, 'Effects of intermittent fasting on body composition and clinical health markers in humans', *Nutrition Review*, October 2015, 73 (10), 661–74, https://academic.oup.com/nutritionreviews/article-abstract/73/10/661/1849182?redirectedFrom=fulltext

34 KA Varady, 'Intermittent versus daily calorie restriction: which diet regimen is more effective for weight loss?' *Obesity Review*, July 2011, 12 (11), e 593–601,

https://onlinelibrary.wiley.com/doi/full/10.1111/j.1467-789X.2011.00873.x

35 Bun-Hee Lee and Yong-Ku Kim, 'The Roles of BDNF in the Pathophysiology of Major Depression and in Antidepressant Treatment', *Psychiatry Investigation*, December 2010, 7 (4), 231–235, https://www.ncbi.nlm.nih.gov/pmc/articles/PMC3022308/

36 Clare Wilson, 'Fasting may boost brain power by giving neurons more energy', *New Scientist*, 11 December 2017, https://www.newscientist.com/article/2156025-fasting-may-boost-brainpower-by-giving-neurons-more-energy/ andv Dale E Bredesen, 'Reversal of cognitive decline: A novel therapeutic program', *Aging*, September 2014, 6 (9), 707–717, https://s3-us-west-1.amazonaws.com/paperchase-aging/pdf/NjJf3fWGKw4e99CyC.pdf

10 Sleep

My sleep had been pleasant to me (Jeremiah 31:26).

Sleep is included as it incorporates so many of the issues that are raised elsewhere in this book. It might seem a strange subject to be included in a book on obesity and being overweight, but it is surprisingly fundamental. As will be demonstrated, a lack of sleep can be caused by obesity and overweight, and can also be the reason for the situation becoming worse.

We will observe what sleep is and the effects of not having enough, before seeing how this all affects our weight.

The process

Sleep is a process that has been designed by God to maximise the restorative processes in our bodies from the rigors of the previous day and to equip us for the events to come in the next day.

It commences with the first stage of being in a drowsy, relaxed state between being awake and sleeping, when the breathing slows down, our muscles are rested and the heart rate declines. It is noticeable that the act of reading a book or magazine accelerates the process of feeling sleepy as the eye movement of going from side to side imitates the eye movement when we are asleep.

The second stage is when we are in a slightly deeper sleep. A sensation may be that we feel awake but we are asleep and just not aware of it.

The third stage is when we experience a very deep sleep when we are difficult to rouse. During this stage, there is the least amount of activity going on.

The second and third stages are referred to as slow wave sleep, which is usually without dreams,

After the deep sleep, we revert back momentarily to stage two before we enter the dream stage, also titled REM (rapid eye movement).

In the full experience of sleep, a person enters all the stages one to three then briefly to two before going to REM. However, going to bed later will result in longer cycles of REM and will disrupt the cycle.

Not getting enough sleep?

The recommended hours of sleep according to age are as follows:[1]

- 6 to 13 years of age: 9 to 11 hours
- 14 to 17 years of age: 8 to 10 hours
- 18 to 25 years of age: 7 to 9 Hours
- 26 to 64 years of age: 7 to 9 hours
- 65 years of age and older: 7 to 8 hours

The issue of sleep deprivation has been described as the new public health crisis. The reality is that millions of people in the world (including 36 per cent of Americans) are not getting the recommended seven hours or more of quality sleep. The result is that those people are unnecessarily experiencing conditions ranging from anxiety, depression and other mental issues to diabetes and strokes and other physical manifestations that are the outcomes of sleep deprivation.[2]

The average person in the United Kingdom spends seven and a half years of their life feeling tired. It is the daily average of two hours and fifty-six minutes of being drained and feeling deprived of energy. In other words, it is the equivalent of nearly four days a month or an annual rate of six weeks. This does not include medical conditions (such as chronic fatigue syndrome) that would naturally cause the symptoms.

There are people who have the sensation of feeling tired from the moment that they wake to the time that they go to sleep. The most common cause are early mornings in a third of instances, while another third emphasises the short days of winter as the cause of tiredness. However, there are also avoidable causes such as insufficient physical exercise and unhealthy diets. It has been found that 18 per cent of people utilised a day of their annual leave allocation because they were too tired to work, while 14 per cent confessed to calling in sick to work so that they could go back to bed and sleep. In addition, 58 per cent cancelled their social life as they were too tired. More worryingly, 30 per cent cancelled any plans to do any exercise as they were too tired, which is the start of a vicious circle as physical exercise rejuvenates and sends fresh supplies of oxygen around the body.[3]

This last point was confirmed by a study, who found that 60 per cent of London workers claimed they were too tired to exercise. It was also discovered that a quarter of respondents do not exercise at all during the week, compared with 35 per cent nationwide.[4]

Although both sleep and exercise are vital to a balanced lifestyle, there should not be the situation where you have to choose between the two and forego one in preference to the other. There is a danger in staying up late and then getting up early to exercise as you will be exercising during your 'biological night,' disrupting your circadian rhythm. The correct amount of sleep is also crucial to resting the muscles (so preventing injury during the physical activity); strengthening the immune system (so you feel like exercising); and preventing weight gain and health issues such as cardiovascular disease and diabetes. Conversely, regular exercise will assist in the preparation of the body to have a good quality of sleep.[5]

APPETITE AFFECTED

Researchers have discovered that insufficient sleep raises the level of a molecule 2-AG in the body that stimulates appetite.[6]

Another study found that people who are deprived of sleep have brains that behave differently regarding food choices.[7] The problem is that the body then desires unhealthy food as it seeks to satisfy its cravings.

WEIGHT GAIN

In a study, it was discovered that sleep-deprived people ate, on average, an extra 385 Kcal daily.

Meanwhile, another study found that children who were aged 3 to 4 years old ate an extra 20 per cent of calories if they were deprived of two hours sleep.[8]

Among adults, those who slept on average 6 hours a night were 27 per cent more likely to be overweight, while the figure for people who sleep on average 5 hours a night were 73 per cent more likely.[9] Indeed, poor sleep results in people choosing higher calorific food to eat—9 per cent higher than they would normally choose in a rested state.[10]

It is not only the unhealthy choice of food that is the consequence of reduced sleep, but also the size of the portions. It has been found that sleep deprivation results in wanting more food instead of maintaining the correct allocation. It has been the experience of many in being handed a large portion of chips (or any other food stuff) and, instead of knowing when to stop, the whole plateful is consumed because we were too tired to persuade ourselves that we have had enough. This example could equally apply to healthy foods as, if eaten in excess, they can detrimentally affect our weight.[11]

It is probably as a result of lower levels of leptin (the hormone that informs the brain that it has consumed enough) and the increased level of ghrelin (the hormone that wants more food). The result is that the less sleep obtained, the hungrier a person will feel. It is estimated that a lack of sleep will result in a 45 per cent increase in the desire to eat more than normal.[12]

Side effects from missing sleep[13]	
Irritability	Increased heart rate variability
Cognitive impairment	Risk of heart disease and stroke
Memory lapses or loss	Increased reaction time
Impaired moral judgement	Decreased accuracy
Decreased creativity	Tremors
Increased stress	Aches
Symptoms similar to ADHD	Growth suppression
Impaired immune system	Risk of obesity
Risk of Type 2 diabetes	Decreased temperature
Decreased testosterone	

It has been discovered that a lack of sleep (and, indeed, too much of it) can lead to a range of health conditions, including high blood pressure or increased cholesterol levels. The study ascertained that

LOSE SLEEP, LOSE YOUR MIND AND HEALTH[14]
Sources: Sleep, Cancer, University Hospitals, The New York Times, The Huffington Post, Annals of Internal Medicine, UC Berkeley, Carnegie Mellon University, European Heart Journal, American Journal of Epidemiology, Drowsydriving.org
Early studies have linked lack of sleep to both colorectal and aggressive breast cancers
Multiple studies have suggested a relationship between chronic sleep deprivation and increased obesity risk
Research has linked short-term sleep deprivation with a propensity to load up on bigger portions, a preference for high-calorie, high carb foods and a greater likelihood of choosing unhealthy foods while grocery shopping

After a while ...	After one night, you're ...
Stroke risk quadruples	Hungrier and more likely to eat more
Obesity risk jumps	More likely to have an accident
Risk of some cancers may increase	Not looking your best — your most approachable
Diabetes risk goes up	More likely to catch a cold
Heart disease risk increases	More likely to get emotional
Sperm count decreases	Less focused and having memory problems
Risk of death goes up	Losing brain tissue
↓	↓
A SLEEP study evaluating 1,741 men and women over the course of 10 to 14 years found that men who slept fewer than six hours had a significant increase in mortality risk, even after adjusting for diabetes, hypertension and other factors	A small survey of 15 men, published in the journal SLEEP, found that just one night of sleep deprivation was linked to signs of brain tissue loss

men who slept for less than six hours a night were at a higher risk of developing metabolic syndrome than those who slept for eight hours.

Metabolic syndrome includes a number of conditions including raised blood sugar levels, high cholesterol levels, hypertension and additional fat around the waist area. The latter point is made by the fact that both men and women who had less than six hours of sleep on a regular basis also had a greater risk of having a larger waist circumference.[15]

INCREASED DIABETES RISK

In many ways, this is linked to the previous point as being overweight and obese increases the risk of Type 2 diabetes; however, the reduction in sleep is also a contributing factor.

The risk is increased to 68 per cent for those people who sleep for less than five hours a night on an ongoing basis (as opposed to a one-off event), especially for those lacking deep or 'slow wave sleep'.[16]

The lack of sleep will also cause more stress hormones (such as cortisol) that reduce the effectiveness of insulin and so excess glucose will be retained in the bloodstream, contributing to the risk of diabetes.[17]

Sleep deprivation

Ariana Huffington has commented regarding burnout, depression and anxiety due to a lack of sleep, particularly among teenagers. It can be caused by waking up often during the circadian cycle, especially in the early hours, as their minds ruminate on all that confronts them (including schoolwork, exams and the pile of papers on the desk), and (as we shall see) the effects that additional weight has on their bodies.

She stated: 'They're fully connected to sleep deprivation. And we see what is happening in colleges—blackout drinking, suicides. These are all connected to people running on empty.'[18]

Wrong drinking

It is generally known that alcohol (with its attendant sugars) can affect both the quantity and quality of sleep, especially as it will not be restful and restorative.[19]

However, caffeine in various guises (whether cola, coffee or tea) can also have a detrimental effect on our sleepfulness.

Travis Bradbery commented: 'Caffeine has a six-hour half-life, which means that it takes a full 24 hours to work its way out of your system. Have a cup of joe at 8 a.m., and you'll still have 25 per cent of the caffeine in your body at 8 p.m. Anything you drink after noon will still be at 50 per cent strength at bedtime. Any caffeine in your bloodstream—with the negative effects increasing with the dose—makes it harder to fall asleep.'[20]

It is advisable to drink non-caffeinated drinks (such as red bush tea, herbal teas or water) after 8 p.m. to increase the chances of a good night's sleep. It is assumed that decaffeinated tea and coffee might be an acceptable substitute, but even these substitutes contain small percentages of caffeine so may not be an aid to sleep.

Snoring

One of the reasons why people do not get enough sleep is because of snoring, which affects more than 30 million (40 per cent) of the UK population. It is estimated that 58 per cent of snorers are between the ages of 50 and 59 years of age and that 40 per cent of men are likely to snore compared to 24 per cent of women.[21]

The reasons for snoring are multiple and include the fact that, as a person gets older, the trachea (airway) gets less room to move as the tongue relaxes and blocks most of the passageway. Allergies could also have an effect.

Other factors which are pertinent to the obesity debate could include: a person being overweight, as the fatty tissue around the neck constricts the airway; smoking, as it causes swelling in the course of irritating the throat lining; and drinking alcohol, as this activity also relaxes the neck muscles more than normal. It could be the vicious circle of being overweight preventing a good night's sleep which, in turn, prevents a healthy lifestyle.

The outcomes can cause drowsiness (due to lack of sleep the previous night), arrhythmia (an irregular heart rhythm), heart attack (as a further outcome from the arrhythmia), stroke (due to the arteries in the neck being restricted) and depression (as the tiredness from lack of sleep will affect a person mentally).

Although there is nothing we can do about our sex, allergies or age, the other factors are preventable. If the primary sources are sorted out then we may be at a much lower risk from the secondary outcomes.

The dangers of not enough sleep

HIGHER RISK OF DEVELOPING ILLNESSES

The inability to sleep well has been discovered to be the source of a whole range of illnesses and disorders. For a start, sleep deprivation will result in changes to 700 genes.[23]

Indeed, a comprehensive review that encompassed 153 studies involving more than five million participants concluded that lack of sleep leads to a high risk of developing diabetes, a reduced immune system, high blood pressure, cardiovascular disease, coronary heart disease and obesity.[24]

HOW MANY HOURS SHOULD YOU SLEEP? HOURS SLEPT VS LIKELIHOOD OF DEVELOPING DISEASE Figures from the Sleep Research Council[22]	
Hours	Likelihood
4−5	30%
6	24%
7	20%
8	20%
9	21%
9−10	26%

What is even more disturbing is that having insufficient sleep even for a few nights in a row will send the healthiest bodies into a pre-diabetic state because sleep is required for the body's ability to control blood glucose levels.[25]

Another consequence of sleep deprivation is that vaccinations are less effective[26] which, together with the suppression of the immune system, will make us more susceptible to colds, coughs, influenza and all the other illnesses with which we will come into contact.

The incidence of developing a cold was nearly three times more likely in people who experienced less than seven hours compared to those who had this allocation or more. With regard to sleep efficiency (that is the difference between going to bed and actually sleeping), those who slept less than 92 per cent of the time they were in bed were 5.5 times more likely to develop a cold than people who slept 98 per cent or more whilst in bed.[27]

Eric Olsen explains: 'During sleep, your immune system releases proteins called cytokines, some of which promote sleep. Certain cytokines need to increase when you have an infection or inflammation, or when you're under stress. Sleep deprivation may decrease production of these protective cytokines. In addition, infection-fighting antibodies and cells are reduced during periods when you don't get enough sleep.'[28]

INCREASED CANCER RISK

With only one night of four to five hours of sleep, the natural critical cancer-attacking cells will decrease by 70 per cent.[29] It includes a marked increased risk of cancer (including bowel, prostate and breast cancers)[30] among people who have reduced sleep due to sleep apnoea (a condition that involves dangerous breaks in breathing while asleep), which might also be the cause of snoring and fatigue.[31] Research has shown that sleep apnoea is more prevalent among people who are obese and so they are at greater risk of the conditions that come with it.[32]

In particular, people who slept less than six hours a night had a 50 per cent higher risk of colorectal adenomas, which have a tendency to become malignant if they are not treated promptly.[33]

Another study discovered the possibility of a connection between sleep deprivation and aggressive breast cancer.[34]

MENTAL HEALTH CONDITIONS AND DISORDERS

A lack of sleep will prevent the brain from making new memories. It is as if the memory inbox of the brain cannot process the experiences of the day. Since sleep occurs significantly later than the learning and original experiences, the benefits of this assimilation will be increased if we take longer to process them. There will be a lack of focus so leading to an increased lack of concentration on the matter in hand—which may have physical manifestations over time (such as going to the toilet).[35]

In research, it was discovered that this integration of our memories takes place at our deepest levels of sleep (Stage 3), so it is important that there is an allowance of time to enable our bodies to achieve this stage.

It is not just the short-term memories that will be affected but that the effects of dementia will mean that the longer-term ones will be affected.

A lack of sleep will mean that there will be an increased level of beta amyloid, a toxic protein. Sleep will usually sweep this protein away (like an antivirus scan on a computer), but the less sleep is obtained then this protein will increase and so will be risk of you developing Alzheimer's and other dementias. The body uses the time of sleep to have the equivalent of a chemical detox. The John Hopkins Bloomberg School of Public Health has shown that less sleep was linked to a greater build-up of beta-amyloids in the brain.[36] Conversely, these proteins will be built up when we have sufficient sleep.

In summary, sleep will assist in the increase of alertness, enhanced memory and promotes learning on some memory tasks.[37]

The impact of this point is that whatever we are determined to learn (be it Bible verses, a new language or anything else), if there is not enough sleep, especially at its deepest levels, then our efforts will be hindered. It does not help staying up late to cram in information—if there is insufficient downtime then the effort will be in vain.

A study has shown that insufficient sleep, together with inactivity during the day, leads to mental health problems, with an increasing risk of clinical depression and bipolar disorder over the lifetime. Other resulting symptoms may include mood instability, unhappiness and loneliness.[38]

EMOTIONAL IMBALANCE

It has been ascertained that just one night of deprived sleep can increase the intensity of arguments with others. The lack of sleep damages a person's ability to gauge emotions, so even the smallest thing can upset the apple cart.[39]

When we are told by God's Word not to let the sun go down while we are still angry (Ephesians 4:26–27), the keeping of this command may be made harder if we have not obeyed His precept to have enough sleep.

INCREASED RISK OF HEART DISEASE, HEART ATTACK AND STROKE

Researchers have discovered that if you are getting six hours or less of sleep, there is a 200 per cent increased risk of a fatal heart attack or stroke.[40]

It is particularly relevant if the people are already predisposed with an elevated blood pressure and poor glucose metabolism. It also affects people living with the condition of atherosclerosis, where the arteries are clogged up with cholesterol.[41] If a person had less than six hours sleep and it was disturbed, there is a 48 per cent increased risk of developing and, indeed, dying of a stroke.[42]

During the period of deep sleep, the cardiovascular system gets an opportunity to be re-energised. The body takes the opportunity to drop the heart rate and reduce the blood pressure, which assists in good heart health.

FERTILITY

Men who are sleeping for only five to six hours a night will have the level of testosterone of someone who is ten years older. The outcome will be that their sperm will not be as good a quality as someone else of a comparable age, which will lead to reduced likelihood of conception. High levels of sleep disturbance for men will lead to a 29 per cent lower concentration of sperm in their semen.[43]

The issue of sleep also affects women's fertility. A study has concluded that 53 per cent of women who slept between seven and eight hours were more likely to conceive, whereas the figures were 43 per cent for those who slept more than nine hours and 46 per cent for those who slept less than six hours.

The reason is that for women who slept more than nine hours the hormone prolactin is produced which inhibits conception. For women who sleep less than six hours, stress hormones such as cortisol prevent pregnancy.[44]

The Benefits of Sleep

As we can see from the issues mentioned, there is much in common with the consequences of obesity and overweightness. The two issues are interconnected as excess weight can contribute to a lack of sleep and a reduction in sleeping hours could result in factors that lead to obesity and excess weight.

It is important that we get enough sleep for, as we have seen, usually eight hours will be beneficial. It has been discovered that a person getting less than six hours of sleep at night is not only at risk of obesity, depression and heart attacks, they are likely to experience effects similar to that of alcohol abuse.

The longer a person remains awake, the brain becomes increasingly less stable and so the attention span diminishes, as does the ability to focus and overall brainpower.[45]

Matthew Walker, a sleep scientist at the University of California, Berkeley, states: 'No aspect of our biology is left unscathed by sleep deprivation. It sinks down into every possible nook and cranny.'[46]

It is a global problem with 17 per cent of South Koreans having at least three nights of insomnia, and nearly 12 per cent of people in Hong Kong experiencing sleeplessness. It was also discovered that 30 per cent of American adults have symptoms of insomnia, including 10 per cent who experience challenges in undertaking their daily activities due to not having real rest.

The same condition is to be found in 20.1 per cent of French people, 24 per cent of Canadian English, 11.7 per cent of Japanese people, 21.4 per cent of Norwegians and in many other countries.[47]

Robert Banks has written: 'Transgressing the environmental rhythms can be an act of unbelief, a reliance upon human works rather than on God's provision.'[48]

CO-ORDINATION

A lack of sleep can result in slower motor skills, which can manifest itself in trips, slips and spills.[49] When we have sufficient sleep, our motor skills will be enhanced so that we will not suffer ill effects from sleep deprivation's consequences. Our mobility will not hinder us or those who are around us and we will have confidence in going out.

Our ability to be an integral part of our church and society can be improved if we have the right amount of sleep because we can be assured of our physical balance.

WEIGHT LOSS

A study suggests that revising your sleep pattern could be a key to looking after your weight.

Researchers have found that sleeping for longer each night could help people reduce their intake of sugary foods and so have a healthier diet.

Part of the research involved half of the participants changing their behaviours so they were enabled to have more sleep, which included avoiding caffeine before bed and establishing a relaxing routine. Interestingly, 81 per cent of those in this group increased their time in bed with half of these increasing their sleep duration.[50]

The principal investigator of the research, Wendy Hall, commented: 'The fact that extending sleep led to a reduction in intake of free sugars—by which we mean the sugars that are added to foods by manufacturers or in cooking at home as well as sugars in honey, syrups, and fruit juice—suggests that a simple change in lifestyle may really help people to consume healthier diets.'[51]

When sleep is reduced or absent, more cortisol hormone (which induces stress) is produced. The outcome is that there is increased glucose intolerance that leads to weight gain. Indeed, the more sleep is had, the less of the fat-storing cortisol is produced.[52]

The people who were prepared to look after themselves by

increasing their sleep duration could be open to better lifestyles, as well as not having the opportunity to munch while they were drowsy!

As stated before, the obesity problem interacts with sleep problems. The Kaiser Permanente Centre for Health Research reported that, 'sleep time predicted success in the weight loss programme'. It was in managing of sleep and stress levels that weight loss became possible, as having too little or too much sleep meant that the battle against obesity was harder. The researchers stated: 'These results suggest that early evaluation of sleep and stress levels in long-term weight management studies could potentially identify which participants might benefit from additional counselling.'

Dr Neil Stanley from the British Sleep Society stated that he agreed with the findings: 'We've always had the eat less move more mantra. But there's a growing body of evidence that we also need to sleep well.'[53]

MOOD

It has been ascertained in a survey that the British adults who completed sufficient sleep were significantly happier than those who did not. The standard amount of time was calculated to be between seven and eight hours.[54]

It was discovered that losing sleep can increase the emotions of anger and aggression throughout the following day. In a study, those people who had reduced sleep had intensified signs of anger and irritability.[55]

It has also been ascertained by researchers at the University of

California, Berkeley, that when we are tired, we are more likely to increase our levels of worry and anxiety.[56] The outcome is so marked that there are doctors who are encouraging patients with anxiety disorders to have sleep therapy as part of their treatment.

STRESS REDUCTION

Sleep will assist the cardiovascular system in recovering from any stressful events that you have experienced. Although your pulse rate and blood pressure will rise during the event itself, the blood pressure will be markedly reduced in the recovery phase compared to those who do not or cannot sleep.[57]

John Piper reminds us: 'God made sleep as a continual reminder that we should not be anxious but should rest in Him.'[58]

The Bible and sleep

There are a few instances in the Bible where sleep is not encouraged, but they are few. The majority of references indicate that we are to receive this gift from God.

Tellingly, there is only one exception in the Bible where sleep at night was not encouraged, which was when the disciples slept in the Garden of Gethsemane after Jesus had requested that they stay awake (Matthew 26:36–46; Mark 14:32–42; Luke 22:45–46). It was a one-off occasion for He knew that there would be plenty of occasions for them to sleep after He had died and risen again.

Apart from that one occasion, God does command us to be awake in order to work—it seems as though the scientists have again been catching up with what is already in Scripture. We now have the scientific basis for what God had already told us:

- Proverbs 6:4—'Allow no sleep to your eyes, no slumber to your eyelids.'
- Proverbs 6:9—'How long will you lie there, you sluggard? When will you get up from your sleep?'
- Proverbs 6:10—'A little sleep, a little slumber, a little folding of the hands to rest.'
- Proverbs 10:5—'He who gathers crops in summer is a wise son, but he who sleeps during harvest is a disgraceful son.'
- Proverbs 19:15—'Laziness brings on deep sleep, and the shiftless man goes hungry.'
- Proverbs 20:13—'Do not love sleep or you will grow poor; stay awake and you will have food to spare.'
- Proverbs 23:21—'for drunkards and gluttons become poor; and drowsiness clothes them in rags.'

However, sleep in the right circumstances is seen in the Bible as the result of honest labour and a reward from God. It can also be seen as trust in the Lord.

- Psalm 3:5—'I lie down and sleep; I wake again because the LORD sustains me.'
- Psalm 4:8—'I will lie down and sleep in peace, for you alone, O LORD, make me dwell in safety.'
- Psalm 127:2—'In vain you rise early and stay up late, toiling for food to eat—for He grants sleep to those He loves.'
- Proverbs 3:24—'when you lie down, you will not be afraid; when you lie down, your sleep will be sweet.'
- Proverbs 6:22—when speaking about the teaching received from our parents: 'When you walk, they will guide you; when

you sleep, they will watch over you; when you awake, they will speak to you.'

- Jeremiah 31:26—'At this I awoke and looked around. My sleep had been pleasant to me.'

God also brings creativity while we are asleep. When He caused Adam to be asleep (Genesis 2:21), God created a wonderful companion called Eve. As it has been noted above, it was a pattern as God allows our brains to think in creative ways while we are asleep, for we were made to be inventive by Him.

It is in the certainty of life that we can sleep, for we can trust God in both our waking and sleeping hours. In Mark's Gospel, Jesus had said to His disciples, 'Let us go over to the other side' of the lake (Mark 4:35). When a great storm arose, the disciples were afraid of their lives, but Jesus knew they were safe and so, He fell asleep (Matthew 8:24; Mark 4:38). It was due to their lack of faith that He rebuked His followers, not because they woke Him up from His shuteye! To demonstrate that the boats would reach their destination, He did quell the storm, which also pacified the agitated emotions of the disciples.

The same trust in God can be seen in the example of Peter, who was imprisoned during a persecution of the early Church by Herod Agrippa. We are told that the apostle was sleeping between two soldiers, who were guarding him (Acts 12:6). He was not sure whether he would be released or not (as the apostle James had just been killed by the sword), but he was sure that his life was in the hands of the Lord, just as the young men in Babylon had demonstrated (Daniel 3:17–18).

God also uses that down time to restore us, physically, mentally and spiritually. An example of this is in the narrative of Elijah who had won a great spiritual battle against pagan worshippers, resulting in the queen putting a bounty on his head. Elijah ran to Mount Horeb where God appeared to the prophet to assure him it is in the small things that we can see God speaking to us. One of the remedies that God gave to Elijah was the gift of sleep (1 Kings 19:5–6), so that he would be built up.

It can be the situation that it is the only time God can speak to us without any distraction. It was in such a time that God showed Abram (as he was named then) a vivid picture of the vision that the Almighty had for the Patriarch's descendants (Genesis 15:12–21). It was the same tactic that God used on Abraham's grandson, Jacob, to demonstrate that the Lord was with him, through a dream where angels were ascending and descending on a stairway to heaven (Genesis 28:10–17).[59]

It is in the times of sleep that God can work in and through us. It is often the best and rarest opportunity as we often resist or ignore Him while we are awake.

Karen Swallow Prior wrote:

> One of the most dramatic events in the ministry of Jesus—and the great test of the disciples' faith—begins and centres on Jesus' sleeping through a storm.

Not only does Jesus admonish us through that story to have strong faith, but his example teaches us also to sleep well.[60]

Lauren F Winner commented:

> Not only does sleep have evident social consequences, not only would sleeping more make us better neighbours and friends and

family members and citizens. Sleeping well may also be part of Christian discipleship, at least in our time and place.

The unarguable demands that our bodies make for sleep are a good reminder that we are mere creatures, not the Creator. For it is God and God alone who 'neither slumbers nor sleeps' (Psalm 121:4). Of course, the Creator has slept, another startling reminder of the radical humility he embraced in becoming incarnate. He took on a body that, like ours, was finite and contingent and needed sleep. To push ourselves to go without sleep is, in some sense, to deny our embodiment, to deny our frail incarnations—and perhaps to deny the magnanimous poverty and self-emptying that went into his incarnation.[61]

We may argue that it is spiritual to burn the candles at both ends, but usually the result is mental, emotional and physical burnout. It is true that we read Jesus prayed all night (Luke 6:12; 22:39–46), but we do not read that it was the usual or even regular practice—its unusualness made it noteworthy because of the enormity of the situation that He was to encounter.

Our experiences

The reality is that we are not divine, for when we lack sleep, our emotions are likely to be fragile as the brain's emotion centres are more than 60 per cent more reactive in this situation. It could mean that we may be unable to place emotional experiences contextually and, therefore, can produce uncontrolled, inappropriate responses to situations and comments.[62]

Don Carson comments: 'Sometimes the godliest thing you can do in the universe is get a good night's sleep—not pray all night, but sleep. I'm certainly not denying that there may be a place for praying all night; I'm merely insisting that in the course of things, spiritual discipline obligates you get the sleep your body needs.'[63]

When we have sleep, we will get a better perspective, a clearer view of the situation—one where the heightened fears and anxieties will have lessened. It is always in the dark hours that the sensitivities of our minds increase and logic can take second place.

It is in the times of sleep that our healthy lifestyles can commence and our discipleship can really take shape for we will only be dependent on God to do His work.

ACTION POINTS

- *Try to get sufficient sleep. Don't watch a tense program on the TV just before going to bed. Shut off all your social media communications. If you are struggling with insomnia, spend the time in prayer.*
- *Avoid caffeine before bedtime and alcohol. Try a hot milky beverage instead. Have a warm, relaxing bath just before bed too if you feel your mind is racing. If you have so many things to accomplish the next day, write them all down before going to bed so you won't worry that you might forget something vital.*

NOTES

1 Elahe Izadi, 'How much sleep do you need? An expert panel releases its recommendations', *Washington Post*, 3 February 2015, https://www.washingtonpost.com/news/to-your-health/wp/2015/02/03/how-much-sleep-do-you-need-an-expert-panel-releases-its-recommendations/?noredirect=on&utm_term=.bb99d4926511; 'How Much Sleep Do I Need?' Centres for Disease Control and Prevention, https://www.cdc.gov/sleep/

about_sleep/how_much_sleep.html

2   *Centres for Disease Control and Prevention*, '1 in 3 adults don't get enough sleep', 18 February 2016, https://www.cdc.gov/media/releases/2016/p0215-enough-sleep.htmlhttps://www.cdc.gov/media/releases/2016/p0215-enough-sleep.html

3   Cited in Gemma Francis, 'Average Briton spends seven-and-a half years feeling tired, study suggests', *The Independent*, 14 March 2018, https://www.independent.co.uk/life-style/average-brit-tired-years-lifetime-sleep-vitamin-d-study-a8255801.html

The top ten reasons for feeling tired were:

1. A sleepless night

2. Having to get up early

3. A late night

4. Dark mornings and evenings

5. Bad weather

6. Too much or not enough exercise

7. Working long hours

8. Busy work schedules

9. A poor diet

10. A large workload

4   Cited in David Gardner, 'We're too tired to go to the gym, say office workers', *Evening Standard*, 13 April 2018, https://www.standard.co.uk/lifestyle/health/london-workers-are-too-tired-to-go-to-the-gym-a3812601.html

5   Karen Weintraub, 'Sleep vs. Exercise', *New York Times*, 8 December 2017, https://www.nytimes.com/2017/12/08/well/sleep-vs-exercise.html

6   John Easton, 'Sleep loss boosts hunger and unhealthy food choices', *uchicago news*, 1 March 2016, https://news.uchicago.edu/story/sleep-loss-boosts-hunger-and-unhealthy-food-choices

7   John Easton, 'Sleep loss boosts hunger and unhealthy food choices', *uchicago news*, 1 March 2016, https://news.uchicago.edu/story/sleep-

loss-boosts-hunger-and-unhealthy-food-choices

8 H K Al Khatib, S V Harding, J Darzi and G K Pot, 'The effects of partial deprivation on energy balance: a systematic review and meta-analysis', *European Journal of Clinical Nutrition*, May 2017, 71 (5), 614–624, https://www.ncbi.nlm.nih.gov/pubmed/27804960

9 The Sleep Council, 'Sleep Healthy', 9 September 2015, https://sleepcouncil.org.uk/sleep-healthy/

10 Reported in: Alexandra Thompson, 'Struggling to lose weight? You may be sleep deprived: Insomnia increases the risk of obesity by affecting our metabolism', *Daily Mail*, 23 May 2017, http://www.dailymail.co.uk/health/article-4533694/Struggling-lose-weight-sleep-deprived.html

11 Pleunie Hogenkamp et al, 'Acute sleep deprivation increases portion size and affects food choice in young men', *Psychoneuroendocrinolgy*, January 2013, https://www.researchgate.net/publication/234884358_Acute_sleep_deprivation_increases_portion_size_and_affects_food_choice_in_young_men

12 See, for example, Stephanie M Greer, Andrea N Goldstein and Matthew P Walker, 'The impact of sleep deprivation on food desire in the human brain', *Natural Communication*, 2013, issue 4, p. 2259, https://www.ncbi.nlm.nih.gov/pmc/articles/PMC3763921/

13 From Dr Travis Bradberry, 'Sleep deprivation is killing you and your career', 19 February 2019, https://www.linkedin.com/pulse/sleep-deprivation-killing-you-your-career-dr-travis-bradberry/

14 Facts in: Laura Schocker, 'Here's A Horrifying Picture of What Sleep Loss Will Do To You', *Huffington Post*, 8 January 2014, https://www.huffingtonpost.co.uk/entry/sleep-deprivation_n_4557142

15 Claire E Kim et al, 'Association between sleep duration and metabolic syndrome: a cross-sectional study', *BMC Public Health*, 2018, issue 18, p. 720 https://bmcpublichealth.biomedcentral.com/track/pdf/10.1186/s12889-018-5557-8

16 C W Kim, Y Chang, E Sung and S Ryu, 'Sleep duration and progression to diabetes in people with prediabetes defined by HbA1c concentration', *Diabetic Medicine*, 22 July 2017, 34 (11), 1591–1598, https://onlinelibrary.wiley.com/doi/full/10.1111/dme.13432

17 Eve Van Cauter, Kristen Knutson, Rachel Leproult and Karine Speigal, 'The Impact of Sleep Deprivation on Hormones and Metabolism', *Medscape*, 19 April 2018, https://www.medscape.org/viewarticle/502825

18 James Barron, 'Not sleeping enough? Arianna Huffington wants to help', *New York Times*, 5 December 2016, p A21, https://www.nytimes.com/2016/12/04/nyregion/not-sleeping-enough-arianna-huffington-wants-to-help.html?smid=tw-nytimes&smtyp=cur

19 Alice Park, 'This is What Alcohol Does to Your Sleep', *Time*, 16 January 2015, http://time.com/3671777/drinking-sleep/

20 Travis Bradbery, 'Caffeine: The Silent Killer of Success', *Forbes*, 21 August 2012, https://www.forbes.com/sites/travisbradberry/2012/08/21/caffeine-the-silent-killer-of-emotional-intelligence/#3701f38e118c

21 Laura Miller, 'Why do people snore? How to prevent it and get a better night's sleep', *Daily Mirror*, 9 April 2018, https://www.mirror.co.uk/lifestyle/health/people-snore-how-prevent-better-12310955

22 Statistics from Rachel Schraer and Joey D'Urso, '10 things to know about sleep as the clocks change', *BBC News*, 28 October 2017, https://www.bbc.co.uk/news/health-41666563

23 Carla S Möller-Levet et al, 'Effects of insufficient sleep on circadian rhythmicity and expression amplitude of the human blood transcriptome', *PNAS*, 25 February 2013, http://www.pnas.org/content/early/2013/02/20/1217154110

24 'Sleep and Disease Risk', *Healthy Sleep* [undated], http://healthysleep.med.harvard.edu/healthy/matters/consequences/sleep-and-disease-risk

25 Maura Kelly, 'Deprivation Nation: How Lack of Sleep Can Lead to Diabetes', *Fitness Magazine*, March 2018, https://www.fitnessmagazine.com/health/conditions/diabetes/lack-of-sleep-can-lead-to-diabetes/

26 Alexandra Sifferlin, 'Why Lack of Sleep May Weaken Vaccine Effectiveness', *Time Magazine*, 1 August 2012, http://healthland.time.com/2012/08/01/why-lack-of-sleep-weakens-vaccine-effectiveness/

27 A A Prather, D Janacki-Deverts, M H Hall and S Cohen, 'Behaviourally Assessed Sleep and Susceptibility to the Common Cold', *Sleep*, 38 (9), 1353–1359, https://www.ncbi.nlm.nih.gov/pubmed/26118561 /

28 Eric J Olsen, 'Lack of Sleep: can it make you sick?' *Mayo Clinic* [undated], https://www.mayoclinic.org/diseases-conditions/insomnia/expert-answers/lack-of-sleep/faq-20057757

29 Rachel Cooke, "Sleep should be prescribed: what those late nights out could be costing you', *The Guardian*, 24 September 2017, https://www.theguardian.com/lifeandstyle/2017/sep/24/why-lack-of-sleep-health-worst-enemy-matthew-walker-why-we-sleep

30 Luciana Besedovsky, Tanja Lange and Jan Born, 'Sleep and immune system', *Pfulgers Archiv*, January 2012, 463 (1), 121–137 https://www.ncbi.nlm.nih.gov/pmc/articles/PMC3256323/

31 Anahad O'Connor, 'Sleep apnoea tied to increased cancer risk', *The New York Times blog*, 20 May 2012, https://well.blogs.nytimes.com/2012/05/20/sleep-apnea-tied-to-increased-cancer-risk/?_r=0

32 Strohl, K. P. (2019, February). *Merck Manual Professional Version: Obstructive Sleep Apnea*. Retrieved August 13, 2020, fromhttps://www.msdmanuals.com/professional/pulmonary-disorders/sleep-apnea/obstructive-sleep-apnea

33 Cheryl L Thompson, Emma K Larkin, Sanjay Patel, Nathan A Berger and Susan Redline, 'Short duration of sleep increases risk of colorectal adenoma', *Cancer*, 8 October 2010, volume 117 issue 4, https://onlinelibrary.wiley.com/doi/full/10.1002/cncr.2550

34 'Lack of sleep found to be a new risk factor for aggressive breast cancers', *University Hospitals*, 24 August 2012, http://www.uhhospitals.org/about/media-news-room/current-news/2012/08/lack-of-sleep-found-to-be-a-new-risk-factor-for-aggressive-breast-cancers

35 William R Klemm, 'How Sleep Helps Memory', 11 March 2011, https://www.psychologytoday.com/blog/memory-medic/201103/how-sleep-helps-memory

36 John Hopkins Bloomberg School of Public Health, 'Shorter Sleep Duration and Poorer Sleep Quality Linked to Alzheimer's Disease Biomarker', 21 October 2013, https://www.jhsph.edu/news/news-releases/2013/spira-sleep-alzheimer.html

37 Sara P Mednick, Denise J Cai, Jennifer Kanady and Sean P Drummond, 'Comparing the benefits of Caffeine, Naps and Placebo on Verbal, Motor

and Perceptual Memory', *Laboratory of Sleep and Behavioural Neuroscience*, University of California, San Diego, [undated], http://saramednick.com/htmls/pdfs/Mednick_BBR_08%5B8%5D.pdf

38 Laura M Lyall et al, 'Association of disrupted circadian rhythmicity with mood disorders, subjective wellbeing, and cognitive function: a cross-sectional study of 91 105 participants from the UK Biobank', *Lancet Psychiatry*, 5 (6), June 2018, 507–518, https://www.thelancet.com/journals/lanpsy/article/PIIS2215-0366(18)30139-1/fulltext

39 Cited in: Sharon Jayson, 'Sleep deprivation plays with our emotions', *USA Today*, https://abcnews.go.com/Technology/story?id=3762648&page=1

40 Michiaki Nagai, Satashi Hoshide and Kazuomi Kario, 'Sleep Duration as a Risk Factor for Cardiovascular Disease – A Review of the Recent Literature', *Current Cardiology Review*, February 2010, volume 6, issue 1, pp. 54–61, https://www.ncbi.nlm.nih.gov/pmc/articles/PMC2845795/

41 Julio Fernandez-Mendoza, 'Impact of the Metabolic Syndrome on Mortality is Modified by Objective Short Sleep Duration', *Journal of the American Heart Association*, 17 May 2017, issue 6, e005479, http://jaha.ahajournals.org/content/6/5/e005479; 'Sleep problems, heart disease often in bed together', Harvard Medical School, May 2007, https://www.health.harvard.edu/newsweek/Sleep-problems-heart-disease-often-in-bed-together.htm

42 Francesco Cappucio and Michelle Miller, 'Sleep deprivation: late nights can lead to higher risks of strokes and heart attacks, study finds', *Science Daily*, 8 February 2011, https://www.sciencedaily.com/releases/2011/02/110208091426.htm

43 Tina Kold Jensen et al, 'Association of Sleep Disturbances with Reduced Semen Quality: A Cross-sectional Study among 953 Healthy Young Danish Men', *American Journal of Epidemiology*, 15 May 2013, 177 (10), 1027–1037, https://academic.oup.com/aje/article/177/10/1027/101677

44 'Trying for a baby? Get seven hours sleep every night and go to bed and get up at the same time', *Mail Online*, 16 October 2013, http://www.dailymail.co.uk/health/article-2462117/Trying-baby-Get-seven-hours-sleep-night.html

45 Farrell Cahill, 'Sleep deprivation: as damaging to brain health as binge

drinking?' *Medisys Preventative Health*, 11 July 2017, https://blog.medisys.ca/sleep-deprivation-as-damaging-to-brain-health-as-binge-drinking

46 Emma Haslett, 'This scientist says the less sleep you have, the shorter your life will be', *City AM*, 25 September 2017 http://msn.com/en-gb/health/mindandbody/this-scientist-says-the-less-sleep-you-have-the-shorter-your-life-will-be/ar-AAsqA6t

47 Ritu Grewal and Karl Doghramj, 'Epidemiology of Insomnia', in *Clinical Handbook of Insomnia*, ed. Hryr P Attirian and Catherine Schuman (Berlin: Springer Science and Business Media, 2007), Chapter 2, pp. 13–22

48 Robert Banks, *The Tyranny of Time*, (Inter Varsity Press, Leicester, 1983), p. 126

49 Monica Christova, Hannes Aftenberger, Raffaelo Nardone and Eugen Gallasch, 'Adult Gross motor learning and Sleep: Is there a mutual benefit?' *Neural Plasticity*, 13 August 2018, https://www.ncbi.nlm.nih.gov/pmc/articles/PMC6110005/

50 King's College London, 'Sleeping for longer leads to a healthier diet', 10 January 2018, https://www.kcl.ac.uk/newsevents/news/newsrecords/2018/01-January/Sleeping-for-longer-leads-to-a-healthier-diet.aspx

51 King's College London, 'Sleeping for longer leads to a healthier diet', 10 January 2018, https://www.kcl.ac.uk/newsevents/news/newsrecords/2018/01-January/Sleeping-for-longer-leads-to-a-healthier-diet.aspx;

52 R C Andrews, O Herliy, D E Livingstone, R Andrew and B R Walker, 'Abnormal cortisol metabolism and tissue sensitivity to cortisol in patients with glucose intolerance', *Journal of Clinical Endocrinology and Metabolism*, December 2002, volume 87 issue 12, pp. 5587–5593, https://www.ncbi.nlm.nih.gov/pubmed/12466357

53 Kaiser Centre for Health Research Press Release, 'Moderate Sleep and Less Stress May help with Weight Loss', 29 March 2011 https://research.kpchr.org/News/Press-Releases/Post/304/Moderate-Sleep-and-Less-Stress-May-Help-with-Weight-Loss;

54 Oxford Economics and National Centre for Social Research, *The Sainsbury's Living Well Index* (London: Oxford Economics, September 2017), https://www.about.sainsburys.co.uk/~/media/Files/S/Sainsburys/

living-well-index/sainsburys-living-well-index.pdf

55   Krizan, Zlatan, Hisler and Garratt, 'Sleepy anger: Restricted sleep amplifies angry feelings', *Journal of Experimental Psychology*, 25 October 2018, https://psycnet.apa.org/doiLanding?doi=10.1037%2Fxge0000522

56   A N Goldstein et al, 'Tired and edgy? Sleep deprivation boosts anticipatory anxiety', *Science Daily*, 26 June 2013, https://www.sciencedaily.com/releases/2013/06/130626143031.htm

57   R C Brindle and S M Conklin, 'Daytime sleep accelerates cardiovascular recovery after psychological stress', *International Journal of Behavioural Medicine*, March 2012, volume 19 issue 1, pp. 111–114, https://www.ncbi.nlm.nih.gov/pubmed/2135966

58   John Piper, 'A Brief Theology of Sleep', 3 August 1982, https://www.desiringgod.org/articles/a-brief-theology-of-sleep

59   A comparable situation can be found when God tells Daniel about the interpretation of King Belshazzar's dream regarding the coming empires (Daniel 8:18).

60   Karen Swallow Prior, 'Want to follow God? Go to sleep', *Christianity Today*, February 2012, http://www.christianitytoday.com/women/2012/february/want-to-follow-god-go-to-sleep.html

61   Lauren F Winner, 'Sleep Therapy', *Books & Culture*, http://www.booksandculture.com/articles/2006/janfeb/2.07.html?paging=off

62   Seung-Schik Yoo, Ninad Gujar, Peter Hu, Ferenc A Joesz and Matthew P Walker, 'The human emotional brain without sleep—a prefrontal amygdala disconnect', *Current Biology*, 23 October 2007, 17 (20), R877–R878, https://www.cell.com/current-biology/abstract/S0960-9822%2807%2901783-6

63   D A Carson, *Scandalous: The Cross and the Resurrection of Jesus* (Wheaton, Illinois: Crossway, 2010), p. 147

11 Exercise

Do you not know that your body is a temple of the Holy Spirit, who is in you, whom you have received from God? You are not your own; you were bought at a price. Therefore honour God with your body' (1 Corinthians 6:19–20).

Role of exercise

It is not enough just to reduce the calorie intake; it must be accompanied by the exertion to get rid of them. There is a memorable saying that 'sweat is fat crying'. The problem with modern living is that we are so sedentary, sweat rarely surfaces.

We acknowledge that although having a wholesome and healthy diet assists in health, exercise also plays a vital part in maintaining your body.[1] It is a two-pronged approach to healthy living, as God has designed us to have a rounded life (but not in the sense of our body shape!).

There has to be a commitment to see regular exercise through, however laborious the exercise can be through repetition (although this may be mitigated by choosing an activity that interests you, such as team sport or being in the open air) and in the getting the equipment together to undertake it. It does not mean that you have to splash out on gym membership, as it could be as simple as getting an exercise mat and doing a class on a social media platform. As Robert H Schuller stated: 'Spectacular achievement is always preceded by unspectacular preparation.'[2]

Sedentary lives

Whereas, as we have observed before, the lack of exercise can be preceded by an increase in weight (as sometimes the cessation of exercise is a precursor to our accumulation of the pounds/kilograms), the good news is that the vicious circle can be reversed by including physical activity as a method to lose the weight gain (together with a calorie-controlled diet). It is necessary to burn off the calories that have been consumed not only in the present, but also in the past.

We live in an age when people are living sedentary lives (particularly in the west) and are having insufficient exercise, preferring to binge-watch on smart televisions with multi-channel allurement or have their time taken up with gaming devices.

It has often been said that, at a professional football (soccer) match, there are twenty-two exhausted men being watched by hundreds of spectators desperately needing exercise. There are many who support their favourite team by wearing the shirt, which can be purchased in XXL sizes in order to cover their pouch, while their sporting heroes are muscular and lean. The situation is often made worse by the spectators shouting out that the players on the pitch should work harder, when they themselves can barely run a couple of metres.

We find ourselves in such bizarre situations, as we live in a world where the mantra is to be as busy as we possibly can. There is constant overwork usually at a desk or table which results in less time and energy for exercise. This baggage is further dragged down by our excessive drinking of alcohol and the consumption of convenience foods.

It has been asserted that people who do not take enough aerobic exercise are more at risk to have or develop high blood pressure; a worrying factor as people in the UK are approximately 20 per cent less active than they were in the 1960s. If the trajectory continues, the nation as a whole will be 35 per cent less active by 2030.

This statistic is backed up by evidence that only 61 per cent of the British adult population (67 per cent of men and 55 per cent of women) aged 16 years and over complete at least 150 minutes of moderate physical activity per week.[3] It means that an estimated 39 per cent of the population (roughly a third) are not even accomplishing the minimum amount of exercise required for a healthy life.

Lack of activity

Researchers have discovered that sitting for long periods increases the risk of diabetes, heart disease and death. Having said that, we need to recognise that harm is still present even if people exercise, as there is no guarantee that physical exercise will result in the elimination of all illnesses and other conditions. We live in a fallen world where sin and its effects are present and we are not immune, however hard we train our bodies. People who have the perfect physiques are still subject to cardiac and respiratory conditions (for example) as everyone else. However, keeping our bodies in good condition reduces the risk.

The Irish Society of Physiotherapists has calculated that the danger of sitting down too long is as serious as smoking was in the recent past, with the possibility of a new health crisis looming. Its research discovered that the 18–24 age group was the least active, with those over 55 years having more physical exercise.

Much of the lower age group activity is spending more time than recommended on screen devices such as smart phones, TVs and laptops/tablets. This inactivity could be damaging as bone density peaks between the ages of 25 and 30 years. So, the implication is that not taking care of their bones in the development period with exercise means there is greater risk of skeletal conditions such as osteoporosis when they are older.[4]

One study calculated that if a person was sitting for six or more hours a day and were exercising for less than 150 minutes a week, they were at a greater risk of dying of a heart attack. However, these risks were offset to some measure if a person exercised for between 150 and 200 minutes a week (See Fig 4).[5]

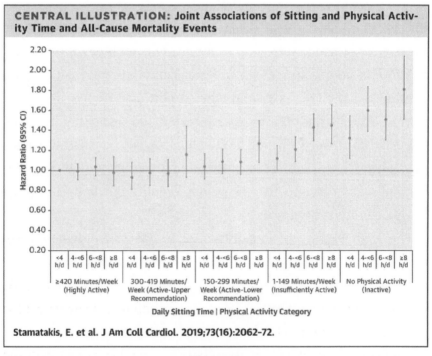

CENTRAL ILLUSTRATION: Joint Associations of Sitting and Physical Activity Time and All-Cause Mortality Events

Stamatakis, E. et al. J Am Coll Cardiol. 2019;73(16):2062–72.

Figure 4

It is important to note that the Physical Activity Guidelines for Americans[6] recommend between 150 to 300 minutes of moderate-intensity exercises for adults, so a person who spends much time sitting should be on the higher end of that spectrum.

Other research states that the opportunities for sedentary behaviour in the modern era, such as watching the TV, sitting in a car or using a computer, are 'ubiquitous'. On average, an obese person sits for two and a half hours more than normal sized people daily, and normal sized people walk two hours more daily than obese people.[7]

The strongest link was between prolonged sitting and diabetes because there were negative effects on the glucose levels and increased insulin resistance.

There are ways to break up our sitting time, such as periods away from the computer, having standing meetings, walking during our lunch breaks and reducing our TV watching during the evenings. It has even been found that people having desks where they have to stand to work (such as those utilised by Sir Winston Churchill when he wrote those great volumes) would be beneficial as it increases the blood circulation and reduces the possibility of fat accumulating in the stomach area.

International research has found that by substituting sitting over a period of six hours for standing would result in the burning of an extra 54 calories a day, resulting in significant weight loss. Over the course of twelve months, this substitution could bring about a 2.5 kg (5.5 lbs) weight loss without changing the person's eating habits, which would project into a figure of over 1.5 stones (9.5 kg) in four years.

The average difference in energy expenditure between sitting and standing was 0.15 calories a minute with the effects being more noticeable in men than women due to their higher muscle mass. In addition, the additional muscle activity is linked to lower rates of heart attacks, strokes and diabetes.[8]

There could be activities during the day that can be undertaken standing up, such as reading or decision-making. In the days of more remote working from home or satellite offices, video calls could be undertaken while standing.

You could make a determined effort to stand up at least once an hour if you are working in a seated position, such as working on the computer. After all, there is the temptation to continue our work until 'we have just finished this part' which never seems to happen as we are still hammering at the particular subject several hours later. It has implications for our social interactions as we go to speak to our colleagues in other parts of the office or even other floors in the building rather than resorting to sending out an e-mail. In addition, there are options for apps on our smartphones or fitness watches that will alert us to move, or we could use the low-tech versions such as a clock or even an egg-timer.

Incidentally, it has been proven that business meetings where the attendees are standing are shorter in time as people do not settle down and get comfortable.[9] These situations not only ensure good stewardship of time, but also the beneficial effects on our health.

Professor Kamlesh Khunti, a diabetes expert at the University of Leicester, commented: 'Exercise is a highly underrated form of medication which, if prescribed more often and earlier in life, would result in more people being healthier, living longer and avoiding long-term conditions. Higher levels of sedentary behaviour are associated with worse health, whereas higher levels of physical activity are associated with better health.'[10]

The aversion to exercise

Research found that respondents preferred to take a pill or drink a cup of tea than take part in any form of physical activity. Indeed, one in four would not exercise even if it meant them living for an additional five years. The only option that was considered to be worse than exercise was a monthly jab. However, some of those in the study stated that they would not have any of the options, even if it meant that they were deprived of an additional five years to their lives.

The researchers also discovered that one in five respondents wanted life expectancy gains beyond what any medical intervention could provide. It was like wanting the elixir of wellbeing without making any contribution towards it.[11]

In addition to revitalising and renewing our bodies, exercising should be seen as a time to enjoy and succeed in those things that matter.[12] A study showed that adults aged 60–90 years undertook more physical activity regularly when there was an emphasis on the increase in the quality of life compared to those who exercised only for health benefits.[13]

Amount of exercise to do

Indeed, statistics from the NHS Direct indicate that 26 per cent of British adults do not even achieve thirty minutes of moderate physical exertion per week. It is no surprise that the net outcome is obesity rates of 58 per cent for women and 68 per cent for men.[14] The unhealthy lack of exercise is reflected in their lifestyle. Only 26 per cent of the adults surveyed by NHS Direct ate the then recommended five portions of fruit and vegetables (although the current recommendation is now that it should be seven to ten portions).

When light to moderate exercise is undertaken six times a week, the average adult feels less breathless. A study has found that more than 25 per cent of its respondents only exercised once a week, while a third would not be able to run a mile '... if their life depended on it'.

In addition, 30 per cent conceded that they were often short of breath after walking up a flight of stairs, while 40 per cent were breathless after running for a bus.

The implication is that being breathless while undertaking normal daily activities could be symptomatic of lung disease. As Mike McKevitt, the Director of Patient Services at the British Lung Foundation, stated: 'There are many people in the UK who may have a lung disease but do not have a diagnosis—who feel breathless daily—but have not been to the doctors.

'Even though more than 4 in 10 people think they're fit and healthy, you can see from the results that this may not be the case,'

The litmus test is that it should take 38 seconds on average for a person to breathe normally again after light to moderate exercise, compared to the current situation when 1 in 20 adults require two minutes.

It is in the small changes, like walking up the stairs rather than taking the lift, or getting off the bus a stop early, that can make a real difference.

In order to combat the growing weight problem, the recommendation is that adults build slowly up to 150 hours of activity each week.[15]

Consequences of inactivity

The Physically Inactivity and Sedentary Behaviour Report found that inactivity leads to increased risk of heart disease as a consequence, which costs the NHS as much as £1.2 billion ($1.5 billion) on an annual basis. The study found that the average man in the UK spent a fifth of his life sitting, which equated to 78 days a year, whereas it was the equivalent of approximately 74 days a year for women.

On a worldwide scale, more than 5 million deaths annually can be assigned to physical inactivity. In the UK, it is the cause of 1 in 10 premature deaths from coronary heart disease.

Conversely, keeping physically active can reduce the risk of heart and circulatory disease by as much as 35 per cent and risk of early death by as much as 30 per cent.[16]

Exercise also encourages the production of endorphins, which enhance the feelings of optimism and satisfaction. The effect is that the hormones of anxiety and tension—that is adrenaline and cortisol—are reduced. Stress is relieved along with its accompanying effects of negativity, worry and detrimental physical effects, such as muscular discomfort, indigestion and pain. It can also reduce the requirement for antidepressant drugs, although medical advice should be sought.

Positives in exercising

Studies discovered that people who exercised twice a week for ten weeks felt more competent socially, academically, and athletically. In addition, they also rated their body image and self-esteem higher than it had been before and had a more positive outlook, which was vital in order to accomplish tasks.[17]

It did not matter what the exercise was, so long as it provided some exertion in movement and in breathing. The scope included a twice-weekly vigorous workout at the gym to a brisk thirty-minute walk—any intense or concentrated activity that would have measurable outcomes for the body and brain. Researchers have concluded that any activity was better than none, although it would have to be significantly more active that reaching out for the television remote control or ambling across the room.[18]

The American Heart Association recommends 'at least 30 minutes of moderate-intensity aerobic activity at least 5 days per week for a total of 150 minutes or at least 25 minutes of vigorous aerobic activity at least 3 days per week for a total of 75 minutes—or a combination of moderate- and vigorous-intensity aerobic activity.' For additional health benefits, they suggest adding 'moderate- to high-intensity muscle-strengthening activity at least 2 days per week'.[19]

People who undertake the recommended 150 minutes of moderate activity or 75 minutes of vigorous activity in one or two sessions a week had a 30 per cent reduced risk of death from all causes, including cardiovascular disease (40 per cent lower) and cancer (18 per cent lower) compared to sedentary adults.[20]

It has been discovered that only 10 minutes of light exercise per day can lower the risk of premature death by 17 per cent in older men (those aged between 40 and 59 years). Although the current exercise guidelines do recommend that a person undertakes 150 minutes of exercise a week in sessions of 10 or more minutes, the new advice would be that a few minutes of activity (such as walking the dog or gentle gardening) would be included as long as the 150 minutes total a week is reached.[21]

It does not matter how the physical activity is undertaken, so long as it is. It does not have to break the bank or leave you needing to apply for a second mortgage as there are many varied ways that the aims can be achieved.

Types of exercise

The various types of activity will have different results:

- Cardio—raises the heart rate and so has a positive effect on the heart and lung health, while also being exhilarating and relaxing at the same time.
- Aerobic—has a positive influence on brain health, including mood uplifts, alleviating the effects of depression (due to the release of natural stress hormones such as cortisol and adrenaline), and could even possibly protect people from age-related cognitive decline.

In the aerobic format of exercise, the increase in heart rate will boost the overall blood flow and oxygen to the brain, so resulting in more alertness and feeling more energetic. There could be a better sleep pattern as you tire yourself naturally. The downside is that, on the day after, there might be delayed onset muscle soreness (DOMS) for about 72 hours, but it is unlikely that it will reoccur so long as the same muscles are exercised regularly.

Over the coming weeks, parts of the cells called mitochondria will be produced at a higher rate, so converting the carbohydrates, fat and protein into fuel for the muscles to utilise as they flex and contract. After six to eight weeks, it has been shown that this production can increase by up to 50 per cent. As the mitochondria increase, you will feel more fit and your endurance will increase.

After six months, muscles will start to show if the workouts are strength orientated. The encouraging news is that the exercise regime would have become a habit by this time. Gyms report that there is a spike of new recruits in January, with the majority of them being gone by the middle of the year, so it is necessary to maintain the fitness programme regardless of how you do it—whether by club membership, app or DVD.

If your exercise is more cardio based, there will be an increase of oxygen being transported to the muscles for fuel, termed VO2 max. The higher the VO2 max then the longer you can run—an example being that an increase of 25 per cent in VO2 max would translate into being able to run 20 per cent farther in the same amount of time.

After a year of regular exercise, your bone will be denser, which is important to reduce the risk of osteoarthritis. Indeed, it has been discovered that regular resistance training combined with aerobic exercise will reduce the effects of osteoporosis after twelve months.[22]

Running, swimming, and other similar activities could also

improve the blood flow, so increasing the energy and oxygen that the body requires.

It is amazing how we can get fit in doing the ordinary things of life (see Appendix C, p. 314), as we embrace those times of walking, but at a faster rate and with more difficulty.

Pregnancy

If women undertake a light aerobic exercise regime throughout their pregnancy, followed by three-weekly sessions after the birth, they experience benefits.

It has been ascertained that they will spend less time in labour with less possibility of the need for an epidural injection. There is also a reduced likelihood of the baby experiencing neonate macrosomia, where the newborn is significantly larger than the average baby.

The researchers wrote of their findings: 'A supervised physical exercise programme throughout pregnancy decreased the duration of the first phase of labour as well as total time of the first two phases together, leading to a decrease in total labour time.'[23]

The use of exercise during the pregnancy could assist the new mothers in returning to their previous fitness after giving birth.[24]

Financial cost

When making cuts in the budget, it can often be the workouts that are the first to be sacrificed. However, a study has been made into the connection between inactivity and the spend on healthcare, which included outpatient visits, other hospital visitations and the costs of prescription medicines.

The participants were asked whether they undertook moderate and vigorous physical activity, which was defined as:

Moderate physical activity causes only light sweating or a slight or moderate increase in breathing or heart rate and would include activities such as fast walking, raking leaves, mowing the lawn, or heavy cleaning. Vigorous physical activity causes heavy sweating or large increases in breathing or heart rate and would include activities such as running, race walking, lap swimming, aerobic classes, or fast bicycling.

The difference between those people with cardiovascular modifiable risk factor (CRF) who undertook physical activity and those who were not as physically active was a saving of $493 (equivalent of £355.00) per year (See Fig 6).[25]

There are the traditional methods of going to purpose-built gyms that have all the required calibrated equipment, but the fees can cost an arm and a leg if you do not have the opportunity to get to them on a regular basis (three or four times a week is usually the time when you get value for your subscription).

There are lower cost alternatives such as joining classes in halls and recreation centres, such as classes on aerobic exercising, Pilates, Zumba or Praisemoves. It could be that your local authority can provide opportunities for physical recreation at a discounted cost, so it might be worth investigating through the local newspapers or online.

In addition, there are programmes that can be accessed through DVDs and social media. You could consider purchasing some equipment (such as resistance bands, mats or small weights), but your home need not look like a mini gym! It is important that, if you go down this route, you check that the instructors are fully accredited. There are so many opportunities to get fit—including apps to download onto your smart phone—that you could easily be dazzled, so get a recommendation for a programme and get started.

It is important to consult with your doctor before starting any exercise regime if there is any doubt about your medical fitness (e.g. cardiac, muscular, skeletal impact). There should be care so that you do not exacerbate any conditions that you already have.

Walking

A benefit of walking is that it reduces the risk of cardiac disease, diabetes, high cholesterol and various cardiovascular diseases such as hypertension and stroke. Indeed, there is some evidence to demonstrate that vigorous walking can expend the same amount of energy as running and is as effective for people with high blood pressure, heart disease, high cholesterol and diabetes.[26]

It is the cheapest form of exercise in that it does not cost anything to do it unless you are hill walking or Nordic walking when the appropriate clothing, footwear or specialist equipment is recommended. The streets, lanes, countryside and coastlines are generally accessible to all, which leaves no excuse left not to participate.

It has been estimated that, if the brisk walk consisted of going at the rate of 4 miles (6.4 km) per hour for thirty minutes, it would use up approximately 150 calories (or the equivalent of a normal sized chocolate bar), which is comparable to playing badminton for the same length of time.

The wonderful thing about walking is that, not only is it good for your physical health, but it also works wonders for your mental health, allowing your brain to rejuvenate and become destressed. I remember, particularly, one office that dreaded me going out for a walk at lunchtime because it enabled me to get away from the situation that we faced, to think through the possibilities, and come back with solutions. It allows you to concentrate on the times when you have to follow navigational directions but, on the long stretches, you can enjoy the creation that God has placed around us so different areas of our brains are activated.

The endorphins (the body's happy hormones), produced during this activity, can leave the person smiling and feeling better. There is more opportunity to take notice of the surroundings—there is nothing better than noticing other people's gardens, especially when they have taken great effort to ensure that it looks attractive.

This activity accelerates the oxygen getting to the brain, which prevents cell death, improves cognitive functioning, and reduces the risk of dementia. If also reduces the risk of having a stroke.[27]

There is also evidence that the risk of dying from cancer is reduced by brisk walking, even when it is in its advanced stages. It was calculated that 25 minutes of active walking a day, together with healthy eating, is sufficient to enable improvements to be made.[28] There are apps available on many Smart phones and fitness watches that take account of the total steps taken in a day, which are a good tool to use.[29]

It is hoped that these initiatives will encourage people to take at least one brisk walk a day with the effects of reducing the risk of early death by 15 per cent. The additional health benefits are the reduced risk of Type 2 diabetes (by 40 per cent), heart disease (by 35 per cent), dementia (by 30 per cent) and some cancers (by 20 per cent).

The whole area of walking is also covered in Appendix C (see p. 314), which further highlights its importance on how you can actually walk your weight off.

In addition, brisk walking can be viewed as literally walking with God, using the time to speak with Him and meditating on His Word. In our 24/7 world, it is so unusual to have time to speak with ourselves, let alone to God, so it is a good opportunity to use this time constructively. It may be just talking with God as in a normal healthy relationship, telling Him what is going on in our lives (as though He does not know already) or being open to what He is saying to us. In the midst of this, God will speak to us away from our daily activity.

Gardening

Gardening can be more of a seasonal activity, but its benefits can be felt all of the year round. There is small motivation to be in the garden in the middle of winter. However, there are still chores that need to be done that can strengthen the body.[30]

The calories that are used in one hour is illustrated below:

Garden activity	Calories per hour
Watering the garden	120 kcal
Planting flowers	200–400 kcal
Weeding the lawn	200–400 kcal
Mowing the lawn	250–350 kcal
Raking the leaves	350–450 kcal
Clearing the garden	400 kcal
Heavy landscaping	400–600 kcal

It is a kinetic activity as it mobilises several muscles at once, especially those in the back, arms, abdomen, buttocks, thighs and hands. Strengthening these muscles will improve your posture and reduce the risk of further injury.

As the muscles around the ankles and feet are reinforced, balance and flexibility are improved, so reducing falls and other injuries.

THE BODY BENEFITS	
HOW GARDENING CAN BENEFIT YOUR BODY	
Part of the body	**Benefit**
Head	Gardeners have lower levels of the stress hormone, cortisol, leading to improved sleep patterns, relaxation and mental wellbeing.
Heart	As a physical activity, gardening naturally helps strengthen the heart, building endurance and increasing stamina, meaning a reduced risk of heart attack and stroke.
Back	Raking and bagging leaves means constant bending, twisting, lifting and carrying—all these strengthen muscles. Just remember to bend at the knees to prevent back strain.
Arms	Cutting back hedges with hand-held clippers not only strengthens your biceps and triceps, but also strengthens your core as you reach up and stretch. Work such as raking and carrying leaves can also tone the upper arms, and increase flexibility and strength.
Abdominals	Weeding on hands and knees, raking, strimming, and starting a mower are all gardening activities which assist in strengthening abdominal muscles and building a strong core.

Simplicity

Undertaking any form of exercise does not have to be onerous; surprisingly, it can include household chores such as vacuuming or scrubbing the floors. As long as the activity lasts for at least 30 minutes a day or 150 minutes a week, it will assist in lowering the risk of death by 28 per cent and the rate of heart disease by a fifth.

Professor Metin Avkiran, the associate medical director of the British Heart Foundation, commented: 'In an age where we're living increasingly busy but sedentary lives in the west, weaving physical activity into our daily routines has never been more important, not only to improve our physical health but also overall wellbeing.

'Increased physical activity could have an increased beneficial impact in lower income countries, due to its low cost and the high incidence of heart disease in those countries.'[31]

It is a good excuse to tackle that pile of ironing or undertake the overdue thorough cleaning of the house—thinking to yourself that this is part of your exercise regime. Who knows, it might lead to a more structured approach to physical activity.

Exercise can be fun

Indeed, one of the ways that we can lose significant weight is by decluttering and tidying up. In a study, it was found that 22 participants lost on average of 10 pounds each in a six-week period just by reorganising their homes, when they combined this activity with moderate exercise and preparing wholesome meals.[32]

Kerri Glassman, a nutritionist, observed that having a messy living area results in having no time for exercise and looking after yourself properly. The effects of having to constantly hunt for items and regularly being in a rush means that the stress hormone cortisol is released, which is responsible for storing fat.[33]

It could be that you see your own house as needing the tidying up or, with the owner's permission, you could reorganise someone else's home so that it looks presentable. You do not have to be a television personality to help a person who has a disability, or who is older, to keep their house tidy, and you will be exercising your body at the same time.

Plogging

Another trend, this time from Sweden, not only helps in exercising but is also incredibly useful in environmental terms. It is called plogging and comes from the term 'plocka upp' meaning to 'pick up'. As you are jogging, pick up any litter that is lying around and dispose of it in the correct manner. Some ploggers go as far as incorporating exercises into the very act of picking up the waste so that their heart rate is maintained at a high rate.

Since plogging requires bending and arm strength to carry the collected litter, it is estimated that half an hour of plogging will burn on average 288 calories, compared to 235 calories from just jogging.[34]

Benefits of exercising

AGE MORE SLOWLY

People who are middle-aged can reverse or reduce their risk of cardiac failure that has been caused by their many years of sedentary behaviour. The solution is drastic as a person would have to participate in two years of aerobic exercise with four to five sessions a week to undo all the years that have been spent sitting or lying down.

The aerobic activity results in an 18 per cent increase in the maximum oxygen intake during the sessions and at least a 25 per cent improvement in the 'plasticity' of the heart's left ventricular muscle, both of which are signs of healthy hearts.

The schedule was as follows:

- The sessions were 30 minutes long, which were accompanied warm-up and cool-down activities at either end.

- One high-intensity aerobic session, such as undertaking four sets of four minutes exercise at 95 per cent of their maximum heart rate followed by three minutes of active recovery at 60–75 per cent peak heart rate.
- Two to three days of moderate intensity exercise (where a sweat is worked up but conversations can be still maintained).
- At least one weekly strength training session.
- At least one long session of aerobic exercise a week, such as an hour of tennis, cycling, running, dancing or brisk walking.

A caveat is that the regime is to be started before the age of 65 years because, after that age, there is reduced plasticity in the heart and it starts to lack the ability to remodel itself.

The added benefits to the increased heart health are that blood cells in the heart are invigorated and that blood is more easily transported to the brain, which then improves the state of the brain.[35]

Women who are fit at 50 years have their risk of developing dementia reduced by five times. The statistics showed that 5 per cent of highly fit women developed dementia, compared with 25 per cent of moderately fit women and 32 per cent of women with a low fitness level. When those in the high fitness category do develop dementia, it occurred eleven years later on average than women of average fitness—occurring at 90 years of age instead of 79.[36]

Further research explored how body size and daily physical activity affected the lifespan of women and men. The physical activities were not onerous in that they included walking the dog, gardening, DIY, sports and cycling to work. The samples were then divided into three groups—those who undertook less than 30 minutes of physical activity a day, those who did between 30 and 60 minutes, those who did between 60 and 90 minutes, and those who did 90 minutes or more. The conclusion was that women who were in the 30 to 60 minutes of daily physical activity group were 21 per cent more likely to reach the age of 90 years than those who did 30 minutes or less.

It was reckoned that an hour of physical activity is the optimum time for women as they do not receive any additional benefit for exercising beyond this amount of time.

However, men who undertook 90 minutes of daily physical activity were 39 per cent more likely to reach the age of 90 years than those who did 30 minutes or less. The study also found that, for men, every additional half an hour of physical activity per day increased a man's chances of attaining the age of 90 by 5 per cent.[37]

Body structure

Like muscles that are under stress, bones act in a similar way. When exercise is undertaken, there is the release of osteoblasts that build new tissue, which in turn strengthens the skeletal structure. It is important as approximately 1.5 million people experience an osteoporosis-related fracture yearly so exercise, such as resistance training, complements naturally the intake of calcium and vitamin D.

Contrary to what has been believed in the past, the occurrence of arthritis among long-distance runners is significantly reduced compared to non-joggers. Unless the participant already has a history of hip and/or knee ailments, there is no link between the activity of running and the possibility of joint pain.[38]

Professor Richard Steadman, a sports injury specialist,

commented: 'If you have not had surgery on your knee, and you're anatomically aligned properly—no bow legs, no knock knees—then you could be running forever. My advice to people is, as long as they're not symptomatic, they should keep on running.'[39]

Indeed, it has been discovered that running helps rejuvenate the body. A study showed that people who ran at least 5.5 miles a week had bone marrow that appeared to be one year younger than their actual chronological age. The better news for those people that ran at least 12.5 miles a week was that there was a beneficial differential of eight years.[40]

Although cycling was discovered to be beneficial, it was running that was the better activity because runners had more repeated cycles of higher spinal loading.

The benefits of jogging for shorter amounts of distance were not ruled out, for regular jogging also helped keep bone marrow young, so you don't need to be a long-distance runner.

The alternative is walking that could be built up through stages, such as walking for ten minutes and then jogging or running for five minutes until you are content to spend more time running.

The idea is that, if it is to be walking then it is to be at a brisk pace and not a casual stroll.

Mental capacity

The power of exercising can be seen in that just doing aerobic exercise (including walking or cycling) for 10 minutes, empowers the brain to focus and solve problems immediately. The responses can be more accurate and the reaction times were up to 50 milliseconds shorter than before. In some cases, there was a 14 per cent gain in cognitive performance.[41]

Even attending just one salsa session (as another form of exercise) can boost your understanding by 8 per cent, focus by 15 per cent and memory by up to 18 per cent.

Professor Michael Duncan, who led the study, remarked: 'Dance is physically active but it's also very co-ordinative. You have to think about the steps, you have to think about the pattern, you have to think about staying in time with the music.

'So that requires a lot of cognitive manipulation while the dance is going on, while you are physically exerting yourself.'[42]

The type of dancing does not matter, so it could be waltzing around the ballroom, all out with Samba or joyously joining in with bhangra. The important thing is that you enjoy it and it pushes you both physically and mentally as you try to remember the steps.

In activities like the ones mentioned before, it is thought that regular exercising of the heart and muscles benefitted those in middle age (that is those people aged 50 years and older) by increasing their thinking and memory skills, even if they were already experiencing cognitive decline. When I have observed activities in care homes, even older people with severe onset of dementia are rejuvenated when the music starts and they are able to reactivate their memories as they participate in the dancing.

Physical activity can be the means of providing the brain with an increased flow of blood, with incorporated oxygen and nutrients in the red blood cells. There is also the boost of a growth hormone that causes new neurones and connections to be created.

The exercise did not have to be strenuous because people become less able to participate in vigorous activity. The moderate action could include the likes of Pilates, Zumba and/or Praisemoves.[43]

Physical activity is increasingly perceived as being important as people grow older, in establishments such as care homes and older people's day centres. It is not only beneficial for their physical wellbeing but also for their mental welfare.

The participation in even the less vigorous forms of exercise can release serotonin, endorphins and other wellbeing hormones in the brain, which will reduce cortisol (the stress hormone) and will, in turn, still the amygdala part of the brain (which senses danger and fear).

However, the best way it seems to protect against age-related brain decline is to participate in aerobic workouts. In the region of the brain where weakened connections have been linked with memory loss, these connections are apparently strengthened. Encouragingly, where people demonstrate symptoms of dementia, heart-pumping exercises that cause much perspiration result in an increase in the size of the hippocampus, the site of the brain responsible for learning and memory.[44]

In a similar vein, incremental physical activity, even doing light exercises, is associated with a larger brain volume and a healthy brain age. It is because individuals have lower metabolic and vascular risks, which feed into better brain health.[45]

Even if a person exercises for one hour a week, it helps to shield them against depressive episodes. Interestingly, the exercise does not need to be aerobic, as people who move without becoming breathless (such as participating in a moderately paced, long distance walk) are appreciatively less likely to report symptoms of depression compared to those people who undertake no exercise at all. It can be recommended that people with severe depression who walk for thirty minutes on the treadmill for ten consecutive days will find it 'sufficient to produce a clinically relevant and statistically significant reduction in depression'.[46]

Another study discovered that five types of workouts were excellent for a person's mental health. Results demonstrated that all methods of movement were extremely effective, including the completion of household chores, which reduced the respondent's poor mental health days by 11.8 per cent. However, across the five types of exercise, it was team sports that reduced the poor mental health days by the most (22.3 per cent), followed by cycling (21.6 per cent), aerobic or gym exercise (20.1 per cent), running or jogging (19 per cent), and recreational sports like basketball or softball (18.9 per cent).[47]

In the rush of modern life, we can become so concerned about the needs and concerns of other people that we can neglect our own wellbeing. It is necessary to take time out to recharge both our physical and mental batteries without feeling guilty about it. Remember: there is only one you, and you will be unable to assist others if you do not take care of yourself.

It is in the slower activity of walking that you can get close to the natural world that God created and, therefore, feel happier as a result. Studies have shown the connection between green spaces and the lessening of crime and aggression, together with less procrastination and a reduced sense of seeing life's challenges as unsurmountable.[48]

Children's wellbeing

Children today spend less time in unstructured play, certainly since the 1990s. It was noted that there has been a shift from previous attitudes of free-range activity (such as playing in local parks, building forts, fording streams and climbing trees) to more solitary, inside activities (such as watching television, video games and organised activities such as clubs and sports organisations). It was commented that: 'We have traded green time for screen time.'[49]

The observation of children missing out on experiencing the benefits of the great outdoors has been noted by organisations, such as the National Trust in the UK, who have promoted an initiative called 50 things to do before you're 11 ¾,[50] which parents and other adults can do in conjunction with the children. The article outlines some of the benefits, which are:

- Better school performance—as time spent in nature and in increased fitness improves cognitive function.
- More creativity—as outdoor play uses and nurtures the imagination.
- Increased levels of fitness—as children expend more energy when they are outside.
- More friends—as children who organise their own games and participate in unstructured group activities are less solitary and learn to interact with their peers.
- Less depression and hyperactivity—as time spent in nature is soothing, improves mood and reduces stress. It can also improve their attention span because activities outside move at a slower pace than they do on the screen.
- Stronger bones—as exposure to natural sunlight helps to

prevent vitamin D deficiency,[51] so enabling children who spend time outdoors to be less vulnerable to bone problems, cardiovascular disease, diabetes and other health issues as they move into adolescence and onto adulthood.

- Improved eyesight—as time spent outside can help combat the increasing diagnosis of near-sightedness.[52] The dependence on screens, especially the use of smartphones, will be detrimental to our optical health, so it is good for our eyes to have a break from the strain that is caused by electronic gadgets.
- Better sleep—as exposure to natural light, together with much physical activity, can assist in the resetting of a child's natural sleep rhythms.
- A longer life span and a healthier adult life—as active children are more likely to grow into active adults, so building on the benefits outlined above.

As a suggestion, my wife and I try to have a computer-free Saturday to motivate us to get out for a walk and give our eyes (and the rest of our bodies) a rest from gadgets that seem as though they rule our lives. It would be good for you and your family to find a way to restore the batteries that is a best fit for your situation.

Setting up for the day

Changing the method of your commute to work can have an impact on your mental health as you start a new day.

A study asked volunteers how they felt about the first 45 minutes of the working day as they went to their workplace. The three modes of transport featured were: driving, cycling, and using public transport.

The researchers discovered that cycling was the best mode investigated, as those who used their bike arrived at the office with 'significantly' lower stress levels.[53]

Dr Stéphane Brutus, the lead author, wrote: 'Recent research has shown that early morning stress and mood are strong predictors of their effect later in the day.

'They can shape how subsequent events are perceived, interpreted and acted upon for the rest of the day.'[54]

Social

As Christians, we should be looking after our bodies in order to honour that which God has given to us. However, there are additional benefits to exercising, particularly in going to the gym, joining a running club, etc. in that we will meet people out of our normal Christian circles.

We can show others that Christians are standard people who are fallen in that we have abused our bodies by lack of exercise and eating unhealthily. But we can also share Jesus and the fact that He has shown us grace by giving us the opportunity to rectify this— such is the power of redemption that God affords to us. We can then use it as a springboard by sharing about the bigger problem (sin) that stops us meeting God and it is a problem that we cannot deal with as only Jesus dying on the cross could deal with sin and its consequences.

If you have church premises, you could consider organising a keep fit class or other activity, not only to ensure that Christians are in good shape, but as a way to reaching out to your neighbourhood. You could also combine it with instruction on nutritious eating, especially if you live and worship in a community that does not have much economically or socially.

Spiritual danger

There is always the danger that we make exercise an idol, instead of the means. In rectifying our worship of food, we can go the other way and think that exercising is the be all and end all. It does not matter if our triceps are tremendous or our abs are amazing; the important issue is that we are keeping our bodies fit. For we recognise that, as Christians, we are stewards for God since He made and now lives inside us by His Holy Spirit.

We are to get our perspectives correct, seeing matters from an eternal viewpoint. Paul wrote to his protégé Timothy: 'For physical training is of some value, but godliness has value for all things, holding promise for both the present life and the life to come' (1 Timothy 4:8). We need to keep these two aspects in mind: there is nothing better than listening to a Christian audiobook or music while in the process of exercising. As God created us to be holistic, we are not meant to neglect one thing over the other.

We can get the balance out of kilter, and in our eagerness to live a healthy life, err too much on the side of caring for our bodies—which can lead to a lie of a different sort. It has been well illustrated in the fictional *The Screwtape Letters*, where the older devil advises the younger one about his human patient: '... keep your man in a condition of false spirituality ... If he must think of the medical side of chastity, feed him the grand lie which we have made English humans believe, that physical exercise in excess and consequent fatigue are specially favourable to this virtue.'[55]

It is possible to have bulging muscles but be undeveloped in our character, so we are to avoid this trap. In all that we do, we should keep in mind that (as in everything else) we should be exercising for the glory of God.

ACTION POINTS

- *Get moving—using either the Physical Activity Guidelines for Americans or NHS England recommendations.*
- *Move more and be less sedentary.*
- *Think about how you and/or your church could set up a low-cost, no contract exercise class, both for your fellowship and for the local community.*

NOTES

1   Kyle D Flack et al, 'Energy compensation in response to aerobic training in overweight adults', *American Journal of Physiology-Regulatory, Integrative and Comparative Physiology*, 315 (4), 13 September 2018, https://www.physiology.org/doi/abs/10.1152/ajpregu.00071.2018?url_ver=Z39.88-2003&

2   https://www.brainyquote.com/quotes/robert_h_schuller_120883

3   *Health matters: combatting high blood pressure* (London: Department of Health, 24 January 2017) https://www.gov.uk/government/publications/health-matters-combating-high-blood-pressure/health-matters-combating-high-blood-pressure ; see also, 'More than 20 million Britons 'physically inactive', BBC News, 3 April 2017, http://www.bbc.co.uk/news/health-39457993

4   ISCP, 'Sitting is the New Smoking', *Irish Society of Chartered Physiotherapists*, 14 September 2017, https://www.iscp.ie/events-and-news/iscp-blog/sitting-new-smoking

5   Emmanuel et al, 'Sitting Time, Physical Activity, and the Risk of Mortality in Adults', *Journal of the American College of Cardiology*, 73 (16), April 2019, 2062–72, http://www.onlinejacc.org/content/73/16/2062

6   US Department of Health and Human Services, *Physical Health Guidelines for Americans*, 2nd edition, 2018. https://health.gov/paguidelines/second-edition/pdf/Physical_Activity_Guidelines_2nd_edition.pdf

7   E G Wilmot, C L Richardson, F A Archana, M J Davies, T Gorely, L J Gray, K Khunti, T Yates, S J H Biddle, 'Sedentary time in adults and the association with diabetes, cardiovascular disease and death: systematic review and meta-analysis', *Diabetologia*, November 2012, 55 (11), 2895–2905

8   Farzane Saeidifard et al, 'Differences of energy expenditure while sitting verses standing: A systematic review and meta-analysis', *European Journal of Preventative Cardiology*, 31 January 2018, http://journals.sagepub.com/doi/pdf/10.1177/2047487317752186

9   For example, Andrew P Knight and Markus Baer, 'Get Up, Stand Up: The Effects of a Non-Sedentary Workspace on Information Elaboration', Social Psychological and Personality Science, 12 June 2014, http://journals.sagepub.com/doi/10.1177/1948550614538463

10 Giles Shedrick, 'Diabetes News: Avoiding "middle-age spread" reduces risk of condition', *Daily Express*, 19 July 2017 https://www.express.co.uk/lifestyle/health/830267/Avoiding-middle-aged-spread-can-beat-diabetes

11 Henry Bodkin, 'Tea or pill preferred over running to combat high blood pressure risk', *Daily Telegraph*, 8 April 2018. https://www.telegraph.co.uk/science/2018/04/08/tea-pill-preferred-running-combat-high-blood-pressure-risk/

12 Michelle L Segar, *No Sweat: How the simple science of motivation can bring you a lifetime of fitness*, (AMACOM, New York, 2015)

13 P Gellart, J P Ziegelmann and R Scwarzer, 'Affective and health-related outcome expectances for physical activity in older adults', *Psychological Health*, 2012, 27 (7), 816–828 https://www.researchgate.net/publication/51595639_Affective_and_health-related_outcome_expectancies_for_physical_activity_in_older_adults

14 Quarter of adults in England 'exercise for less than half hour a week', *The Guardian*, 30 March 2017, https://www.theguardian.com/society/2017/

mar/30/quarter-adults-less-half-hour-exercise-nhs-obesity-inactivity-five-portions; Sophie Borland, 'A quarter of adults can't even manage a weekly half-hour walk: Sedentary lifestyle of Britons laid bare by new NHS figures', *Daily Mail*, 31 March 2017, http://www.dailymail.co.uk/health/article-4366506/A-quarter-adults-t-manage-weekly-half-hour-walk.html, NHS Digital, *Statistics on Obesity, Physical Activity and Diet—England, 2017* (London: NHS, 30 March 2017) http://digital.nhs.uk/catalogue/PUB23742

15 Chief Medical Officers, *Start Active, stay active: a report on physical activity from the four home countries* (London: Department of Health, 2011) https://www.gov.uk/government/publications/start-active-stay-active-a-report-on-physical-activity-from-the-four-home-countries-chief-medical-officers

16 British Heart Foundation, *Physical Inactivity and Sedentary Behaviour Report 2017*, April 2017 https://www.bhf.org.uk/publications/statistics/physical-inactivity-report-2017

17 Dr Travis Bradberry, *Eight things ridiculously successful people do before 8 a.m.* http://www.talentsmart.com/articles/8-Things-Ridiculously-Successful-People-Do-Before-8-AM-872382211-p-1.html

18 Pedro F Saint-Maurice, Richard P Troiano, Charles E Matthews and William E Kraus, 'Moderate-to-Vigorous Physical Activity and All-Cause Mortality: Do Bouts Matter', *Journal of the American Heart Association*, volume 7 issue 6, 22 March 2018, http://jaha.ahajournals.org/content/7/6/e007678

19 American Heart Association, 'American Heart Association Recommendations for Physical Activity in Adults', 14 December 2014, https://www.heart.org/HEARTORG/HealthyLiving/PhysicalActivity/FitnessBasics/American-Heart-Association-Recommendations-for-Physical-Activity-in-Adults_UCM_307976_Article.jsp#.WAkmMtyBKVt

20 Cited in: Cheryl S Grant, 'Here's Why It's OK to Work Out Only on Weekends', *Reader's Digest*, 29 January 2017, http://www.msn.com/en-gb/health/fitness/here%E2%80%99s-why-it%E2%80%99s-ok-to-work-out-only-on-weekends/ar-AAmkJcf

21 Study by the British Regional Heart Study, https://www.ucl.ac.uk/pcph/research-groups-themes/brhs-pub/tools/pdfs/keyfindings30yr; cited in:

Shivali Best, 'Just 10 MINUTES of light exercise can lower death risk in older men, study finds', *Daily Mirror*, 6 March 2018; British Medical Journal, 'Just a few minutes of light intensity exercise linked to lower death risk in older men', *Medical Press*, 19 February 2018 https://medicalxpress.com/news/2018-02-minutes-intensity-linked-death-older.html

22 Uma Sharma, 'What happens to your body when you start exercising regularly', *Business Insider*, 30 January 2018, https://www.businessinsider.com/benefits-of-regular-exercise-2018-1?r=US&IR=T

23 Reuben Barakat, Evelia Franco, Maria Perales, Carmina Lopez and Michelle F Mottola, 'Exercise during pregnancy is associated with a shorter duration of labour. A randomised clinical trial', *European Journal of Obstetrics and Gynaecology and Reproductive Biology*, May 2018, volume 224, pp. 33–40, http://www.ejog.org/article/S0301-2115(18)30096-4/abstract

24 Ibid.

25 Javier Valero-Elizondo et al, 'Economic Impact of Moderate-Vigorous Physical Activity Among Those With and Without Established Cardiovascular Disease: 2012 Medical Expenditure Panel Survey', *Journal of the American Heart Association*, 2016, http://jaha.ahajournals.org/content/5/9/e003614.short?rss=1&source=mfr

26 Paul T Williams and Paul T D Thompson, 'Walking vs running for hypertension, cholesterol, & diabetes risk reduction', *Arteriosclerosis, Thrombosis and Vascular Biology*, May 2013, 33 (5), 1085–1091, https://www.ncbi.nlm.nih.gov/pmc/articles/PMC4067492/

27 New Mexico Highlands University, 'Research shows walking increases blood flow in the brain', 24 April 2017, http://www.nmhu.edu/research-shows-walking-increases-blood-flow-brain/

28 Cited in: Jane Kirby, 'Brisk walk each day may cut risk of death from cancer', *The Independent*, 6 June 2017, https://www.independent.co.uk/news/health/cancer-study-risk-walking-death-exercise-research-a7774041.html

29 Such as https://www.nhs.uk/oneyou/active10/home#7jwsEt4sYmhFDqXh.97

30 Research by AXA PPP cited in: Sarah Chaudry, 'This is what spending one hour in the garden does to your body', *Country Living*, 30 May 2017,

https://www.countryliving.com/uk/wellbeing/a645/hour-gardening-health-benefits/

31 'Vacuuming and scrubbing the floor are enough exercise to protect heart and extend life, study finds', *The Daily Telegraph*, 21 September 2017, https://www.telegraph.co.uk/news/2017/09/21/vacuuming-scrubbing-floor-enough-exercise-protect-heart-extend/

32 Peter Walsh, *Lose the Clutter, Lose the Weight* (New York: Rodale Books, 2015), p. 4

33 Yolanda Zaw, 'One simple trick to lose 10 pounds without dieting at all', https://evoke.ie/2018/01/01/health/fit/one-simple-trick-to-lose-10-pounds-without-dieting-at-all, 1 January 2018

34 Chelsea Ritschel, 'Plogging: the popular new eco-friendly workout', *The Independent*, 29 March 2018, https://www.independent.co.uk/life-style/plogging-sweden-rubbish-garbage-litter-exercise-health-workout-a8278656.html

35 Shigeki Shibata et al, 'The effect of lifelong exercise frequency on arterial stiffness', *The Journal of Physiology*, 20 May 2018, https://physoc.onlinelibrary.wiley.com/doi/abs/10.1113/JP275301

36 Helena Hörder et al, 'Midlife cardiovascular fitness and dementia—A 44-year longitudinal population study in women', *Neurology*, 14 March 2018, http://n.neurology.org/content/neurology/early/2018/03/14/WNL.0000000000005290.full.pdf

37 Lloyd Brandts and Piet A van den Brandt, 'Body size, non-occupational physical activity and the chance of reaching longevity in men and women: findings from the Netherlands Cohort study', *Journal of Epidemiology and Community Health*, January 2019, https://jech.bmj.com/content/early/2019/01/05/jech-2018-211410

38 Danielle Y Ponzio et al, 'Low Prevalence of Hip and Knee Arthritis in Active Marathon Runners', *The Journal of Bone and Joint Surgery*, 17 January 2018, 100 (2), 131, https://www.jbjs.org/reader.php?source=The_Journal_of_Bone_and_Joint_Surgery/100/2/131/abstract&id=31000&rsuite_id=1543418#info

39 Henry Bodkin, 'Long distance running is good for your knees, study claims', *Daily Telegraph*, 3 February 2018, https://www.telegraph.co.uk/news/0/long-distance-running-good-knees-study-claims/

40 Daniel L Belevy et al, 'Specific Modulation of Vertebral Marrow Adipose Tissue by Physical Activity', *Journal of Bone and Mineral Research*, 33, (4), April 2018, 651–657, https://onlinelibrary.wiley.com/doi/epdf/10.1002/jbmr.3357?referrer_access_token=Kvywcma1FnPGBcoxswjGQk4keas67K9QMdWULTWMo8MTCdUOXQvDjIskuf_J1NNsQG93WEWmgs211Z5xrduOk8s3AzgBj-xenteJExplw687g0J3j0TRN3ia4HwkeUF5bw1FQ-ziew-EkwJsa7XvPJ8JKN1PcOqFawqChyR4Lm6E1mcLuEtG-MqwvrFps03tspuGVaQEDWi9YVYxrtftSFjRA2B0a20GeLNSJpx_XTWlxD5BtxKN_J58mq2dL-g4&

41 A Samari, M Heath, 'Execution-related oculomotor control is improved following 10-min single-bout of aerobic exercise: Evidence from the antisaccade task', *Neuropsychologia*, 8 January 2018, pp. 73–81, https://www.ncbi.nlm..nih.gov/pubmed/29191783;

42 Cited in Francesca Rice, 'Dancing can boost your brainpower and memory, says science', *Prima*, 5 January 2018, http://www.prima.co.uk/diet-and-health/exercise/news/a42453/salsa-dancing-boosts-brainpower-memory/

43 Joseph Michael Northey, Nicholas Cherbuin, Kate Louise Pumpa, Disa Jane Smee and Ben Rattray, 'Exercise interventions for cognitive function in adults older than 50: a systematic review with meta-analysis', *British Journal of Sports Medicine*, 52 (3), http://bjsm.bmj.com/content/bjsports/52/3/154.full.pdf

44 Erin Brodwin, 'There's even more evidence that one type of exercise is the closest thing to a miracle drug that we have', *Business Insider Australia*, 19 December 2017, https://www.businessinsider.com/best-exercise-for-brain-body-2017-7?r=US&IR=T

45 Boston University School of Medicine, 'Light, physical activity reduces brain ageing', 19 April 2019, https://www.eurekalert.org/pub_releases/2019-04/buso-lpa041719.php

46 Erin Brodwin, 'There's even more evidence that one type of exercise is the closest thing to a miracle drug that we have', *Business Insider Australia*, 19 December 2017, https://www.businessinsider.com/best-exercise-for-brain-body-2017-7?r=US&IR=T

47 Sammi R Chekrod et al, 'Association between physical exercise and mental health in 1.2 million individuals in the USA between 2011 and 2015: a cross-sectional study', *The Lancet Psychiatry*, 5 (9), 1 September

2018, pp. 739–746,, https://www.thelancet.com/journals/lanpsy/article/PIIS2215-0366(18)30227-X/fulltext

48 Studies by Frances Kuo and others cited in: Florence Williams, *The Nature Fix: Why Nature makes us happier, healthier and more creative* (London: W Norton and Co, 2017)

49 Collin O'Mara, 'Kids do not spend nearly enough time outside. Here's how (and why) to change that', *Washington Post*, 29 May 2018, https://www.washingtonpost.com/news/parenting/wp/2018/05/30/kids-dont-spend-nearly-enough-time-outside-heres-how-and-why-to-change-that/?utm_term=.24699f00cb00

50 https://www.nationaltrust.org.uk/50-things-to-do

51 Royal National Orthopaedic Hospital NHS Trust, 'Vitamin D in Children', https://www.rnoh.nhs.uk/services/children-and-adolescents/vitamin-d-children

52 Reuters Health, 'Outdoor time may protect kids from near-sightedness', *Reuters*, 5 February 2009, https://www.reuters.com/article/us-outdoor-nearsightedness/outdoor-time-may-protect-kids-from-nearsightedness-idUSTRE5146C920090205

53 J Coady, 'New Research: Feeling stressed? Bike to work', *Concordia University*, 21 June 2017, http://www.concordia.ca/cunews/main/stories/2017/06/21/new-research-feeling-stressed-bike-to-work-jmsb.html

54 Stéphane Brutus et al, 'Cycling, car, or public transport: a study of stress and mood upon arrival at work', *International Journal of Workplace Health Management*, 10 (1), 2017, 13–24, https://www.emeraldinsight.com/doi/abs/10.1108/IJWHM-10-2015-0059

55 C S Lewis, *The Screwtape Letters* (London: Harper Collins, 1998), p. 67

12 Social implications

> You have lived on earth in luxury and self-indulgence. You have fattened yourselves as in a day of feasting (James 5:5, alternative reading).

It is an interesting conundrum as to whether those who are supporting the exploited poor or are concerned about the effects of intensive farming would eat items (such as beef burgers) which were made as a result of those activities. There seems to a disconnect, particularly in the western mindset, between the food on our plates and the effects on the land and the people who produce it.

The demand for more and cheaper food is the result of what John Sentamu, the former Archbishop of York, has called 'rapacious consumer appetite'. He told the Institute of Jewish Policy Research that such an attitude has been developed at the expense of the inbuilt sense of responsibility. Dr Sentamu stated: 'Seemingly unfettered rights and entitlements have come to the fore whilst responsibility has not simply gone out of fashion but seems to have fallen off the radar.'

He continued: 'Our society needs once more to rediscover the compassion and service at the heart of religion.'[1]

Kent Carlson and Michael Lueken have observed: 'In order to help people follow Christ more fully, we would have to work against the very methods we were using to attract people to our church ... we slowly began to realise that, to be faithful to the gospel of Jesus, consumerism was not a force to be harnessed but rather an anti-biblical value system that had to be prophetically challenged.'[2]

We can easily forget the growing impact that poverty can have in the world. There is the reminder that: 'In 1820 the gap between the richest and the poorest countries was about four to one. In 1913, it was 11 to one, and in 1950 it was 35 to one. By 2002 ... the gap was 75 to one.'[3]

The transitory nature of consumerism can be summed up in the words of Peggy Noonan: 'I think we have lost the old knowledge that happiness is overrated—that, in a way, life is overrated. We have lost, somehow, a sense of mystery—about us, our purpose, our meaning, our role. Our ancestors believed in two worlds, and understood this to be the solitary, poor, nasty, brutish and short one. We are the first generations of man that actually expected to find happiness here on earth, and our search for it caused such unhappiness. The reason: If you do not believe in another, higher world, if you believe only in the flat material world around you, if you believe that this is your only chance of happiness—if that is what you believe, then you are not disappointed when the world does not give you a good measure of its riches, you are despairing.'[4]

When we seek cheap food, obtained at the expense of people and the planet, we are demonstrating that our practices do not follow our beliefs. If we believe that God created all people to be equal and the resources of this world are to be used responsibly, why do we hanker after goods that are produced at cut prices so other people are exploited and forests are destroyed for crops and animals to be raised in bulk?

It is within the power of the western Christians to do something about the inequality. Rick Sterns has written: 'The total income of American churchgoers is $5.2 trillion. (That's more than $5,000 billion.) It would take just a little over 1 per cent of the income of American Christians to lift the poorest 1 billion people out of extreme poverty. Said another way, American Christians, who make up about 5 per cent of the Church worldwide, control about half of global Christian wealth; a lack of money is not our problem.'[5]

When the money, that is consumed in takeaways and fast food, is taken into account, Christians have a particular responsibility in ensuring that other people are not exploited and, indeed, are taken out from their crippling circumstances of poverty and enslavement. The reason is that we are all made in the image of God, so we have a duty to reflect His higher desire for our lives. Where we demonstrate otherwise, we are showing contempt at the parts of Scripture that we feel do not apply to us (despite our mouths saying that all the Bible is relevant) and showing that in our hearts' attitude not all lives matter—we are declaring that we and our desires take precedence over everything else.

The environment and the humiliating conditions that people find themselves in are the result of man's desire to be god and the resulting curse (Genesis 3:16–19). It does not mean that those people are personally responsible for the situation in which they find themselves, but that it is the consequence of the whole of humanity turning its back on the Creator. The effects of our gluttony can be experienced adversely in another country thousands of miles away.

We should be concerned for the welfare of others and not simply say, 'Am I my brother's keeper?' (Genesis 4:9). Where there is injustice, hardship and poverty, leading to a lower life expectancy, because of our behaviour (including our spending), the response is 'yes' for their cries are heard by the Lord and we become accountable.

In contrast, when we do something to raise the status of other people, we have an opportunity to worship God. Jesus commented that, 'you will always have the poor among you' (John 12:8), not so that we would be complacent, but that we would lift our eyes off our own situation and help others. The outcome will be that our thoughts are raised even higher to the One who made us, rules over creation and has given something of His provision so that we could walk with those who do not have the same economic status as ourselves.

We have been granted stewardship over creation by God, which means that we are to conduct ourselves as careful stewards and not be merely consumers. We have become so used to a hedonistic worldview; indeed, we have bought into it ourselves. The narcistic thinking that 'it is all about me' has infiltrated our lives and that of our churches so that God's perspective on His creation is no longer considered to be relevant. We would rather chomp on a steak than consider the impact that bringing that meat to our plate has had on our environment.

Environment

When God said that we were take dominion over the world, He did not mean us to eat it all! And yet, we seem to be preoccupied with getting cheap, unhealthy food regardless of cost—on the land, on suppressed peoples, even on our bodies.

It is ironic that we, the people of the more well-off generation, who are rightly concerned about the environment and how we treat what God has created, can become blind to the responsibility on a personal level to look after our bodies. So, we create more pollution through the amount of plastics produced to wrap around the food and the increased carbonisation of the atmosphere through their transportation.

The overreliance on convenience foods has caused the increase in plastics, especially the non-biodegradable versions. Our intake of fast and convenience food is found in the litter on our roadsides when the containers of mass-produced sandwiches are thoughtlessly discarded, or even deposited in landfill sites where they will sit for thousands of years—if they are ever broken down at all. I am not implying that we revert back to the experiences of previous generations when produce was sold in paper bags and milk was supplied in bottles (or, as in even earlier generations, in containers provided by the purchaser), but it could make us think more about how our food consumption impacts the planet that we live on.

We often act as though we are the owners of the world when, in fact, we should realise that our real role is that of being stewards. The owner is the God who created it, which His Word makes clear—'The earth is the LORD's, and everything in it, the world, and all who live in it' (Psalm 24:1). We import cheap food stuffs without due regard of the air miles that it takes to transport it—the skies are filled with planes which are flying just to fulfil our consumer appetite.

It is no accident that the scourge of litter on our highways and byways comes mainly from our desire for fast food and ready meals. It is another example of our unhealthy desires defacing the perfect creation that God made. Even in the Extermination Revolution (an environmental campaign group) disruptions throughout London and other UK cities in 2019, there was the debris of single-use plastic from food and drink left behind, in contradiction to their stated aims.

The global deforestation and the increase of plastic in our oceans (particularly discarded fishing nets) are, whether secular ecologists and environmentalists like it or not (especially if they are adherents of scientism), further evidence of our sinful nature. It is part of the 'I want' mentality, when we have placed our desires as the ultimate, instead of seeking to enthrone God in the centre of our lives.

It is true that creation is seeking to be restored from the impact of our sin (Romans 8:20–21), but that time has yet to come. When God created the world, He said that 'it was very good' (Genesis 1:31), and we have kicked it around so that it is destroyed beyond its original intent—which was to reflect the beauty of and to give glory to God.

The problem could be accelerating as it has been estimated that the world's population could reach 10 billion by 2050.[6] This scenario could result in the environmental costs of the food system rising by as much as 90 per cent over the next two decades.

Dr Marco Springmann, from the Nuffield Department of Population Health at the University of Oxford, has commented on the exceeding of the planetary boundaries (i.e. the level to which human actions destabilise the Earth's ecosystem): 'Without concerted action, we found that the environmental impacts of the food system could increase by 50 to 90% by 2050 as a result of population growth and the rise of diets high in fats, sugars and meats.'[7]

There is an implication for greenhouse gases as people who are overweight and obese eat more food, and food production accounts for 20 per cent of global emission rates. The growth in population can be managed if all of us eat responsibly—it seems as though we are already consuming the food that would be required if there were more people on the planet. If we reduce the amount that we consume to a reasonable and healthy level, the problem of climate change, as caused by our consumer society, will be reduced.

If other costs for producing food are factored in (such as manufacturing, production, processing, transportation, marketing and consumption), food production accounts for approximately 30 per cent of global energy consumption.[8] The reserves of gas and oil are not infinite and the extractable sources will be non-existent by the end of the twenty-second century (with an estimate of oil being depleted in 53 years, natural gas in 54 years and coal in 110 years, i.e. less than 200 years after we had started using them), while electricity from renewable sources are presently unable to sustain the current demands. Within that framework, we need to save energy by all means possible, even if it means that we are to cut down on our food consumption.

The farming of livestock is the most energy-utilised industry in the world—more than transportation, mining and logging. It has been calculated that livestock production is responsible for 18 per cent of all greenhouse gases.[9]

The production of 1kg of lamb results in the emission of 33.06 kg of carbon dioxide (CO_2), one kilogram of beef results in 32.49 kg of CO_2, whereas one kilogram of vegetables would result in just 0.06 kg of CO_2.[10]

In addition, the move to a less meat orientated diet would reduce the use of cropland, fresh water and fertiliser by as much as 25 per cent.[11]

From livestock methane emissions alone, there is 11 per cent more methane in the atmosphere than previously estimated.

Cattle and other ruminant animals release methane into the atmosphere as a result of enteric fermentation—in other words, the digestive process that takes place within their stomachs. Surprisingly, it is the gas released from exhaling or belching that makes the most difference.

Julie Wolf, the lead author of a report on the subject, has stated: 'In most developed regions, the livestock have been bred to be larger—they are more productive, especially with dairy cows. And that will result in a larger estimate of methane emitted by each animal.'

The report does emphasise that livestock methane emissions, while not being the dominant cause of global methane emissions, could be a major contributor to the observed annual emissions increases over the 2000s to 2010s. However, it could be controlled by means such as changing the animals' diets and radically reducing the voluminous human food waste.[12]

In addition, it takes eleven times more fossil fuel to produce animal protein than it does plant protein.[13]

The deforestation of our planet has taken place at the expense of our environment—destroying communities, increasing the loss of animal species and ruining the atmosphere. According to the latest statistics, the loss of the Amazon rainforest has accelerated to its highest rate in a decade, being 13.7 per cent over the previous year's statistics. It was reported that approximately 7,900 sq. km (3,050 sq. miles) were destroyed between August 2017 and July 2018—the equivalent of an area five times the size of London. Although illegal logging was blamed, it was no coincidence that most of the deforestation occurred in the Brazilian states where grain is produced, so agriculture could also be a factor in the denuding of this asset.[14]

It is not only land that is under threat. Water that is essential for all, especially the smallholders, to grow their produce has become contaminated in many instances. An example is CAFOD's partners in Paraguay who reported that water sources had been compromised by soya growers utilising agro-chemicals. As many smallholders will experience, the daily grind of travelling to obtain water so that their crops can grow is an activity that will take many hours, caused by drought and industrial processes. Where communities lack access to and control over their own land, water supply and other important resources (such as seeds and natural fertilisers), there will always be the struggle for them to grow enough to eat and sell.[15]

It is in the matters we might not think much about that can make all the difference. The University of Manchester has looked at forty different sandwich types, recipes and combinations. It was ascertained that sandwiches with pork meat (such as bacon, ham or sausages), cheese or prawns had the highest carbon footprints. The most carbon intensive sandwich was the all-day breakfast, consisting of egg, bacon and sausage, which generated 1441 grams of carbon dioxide equivalent (CO2 equ) and is comparable to driving twelve miles in a car.

The sandwich with the lowest carbon emission equivalent was the homemade ham and cheese. It is important because, according to the British Sandwich Association (BSA), there were 11.5 million sandwiches eaten in the UK each year, half of which were homemade and the other half are sold in shops, supermarkets and service stations. The total amount of sandwiches equates, on average, to 9.5 million tonnes of CO2 equ annually—comparable to 8.6 million cars being driven.

The largest contributor to the carbon footprint is the agricultural production and processing of the ingredients, which can account for approximately 37–67 per cent of the carbon dioxide equivalent for ready-made sandwiches, depending on the type. A further quarter of the carbon footprint is taken by the chilled cabinets in stores where the items are displayed. The packaging material makes up a further 8.5 per cent and the final 4 per cent is the result of transportation and keeping the sandwiches refrigerated in transit.

The study came to the conclusion that the carbon footprint of just these food items could be reduced by as much as 50 per cent if there were changes to the recipes, packaging and waste disposal.[16]

If we disregard such evidence, we can tend gardens and join good societies for preservation and conservation (including those for birds and horticulture) and yet at the same time be destroying environments hundreds of miles away because of our eating habits. When we are walking around parks and natural sites, we could still be inflicting harm on the planet as we consume ready-made sandwiches and other snacks that have caused harm to the wider environment.

The solid application of the creation narrative is that we are stewards for this generation—and all future generations—of the resources that God has given to us.

When Paul wrote about creation being 'liberated from its bondage to decay' (Romans 8:21), he was not just referring to the thistles and thorns on one hand and to earthquakes and other natural disasters on the other. Humanity has clearly had a hand in this decay by provocative actions, such as destroying rain forests, depriving creatures of their natural habitats, polluting both the sea and land with life-destroying and debilitating plastics, and the list goes on. The reason for these actions can be seen in its root: greed. We want products, with food being a primary cause, to be sourced cheaply and with the easiest of transportation so that we can have it on our plates without the inconvenience of delving too deeply into our bank balances.

Sir Lauren van der Post has written poignantly:

> For we are none of us right; we do not know ourselves sufficiently. We have not faced up to the fact that we ourselves, not our institutions or stars, are the source of the error, and that until we have dealt with the error in ourselves we cannot deal properly with what is wrong with the world.[17]

Another secular writer, Jeremy Griffith (an Australian biologist), has also recognised the depravity of man as causing the destruction of the environment. He wrote: 'The issue of the human condition has been the real, underlying issue we needed to solve if we were to exonerate and thus rehabilitate the human race [. We] have been so fearful and insecure about the subject that instead of confronting it and trying to solve it we have been preoccupied denying and escaping it. The truth is that while much attention has been given to the need to love each other and the environment if we are to 'save the world', the real need if we were to actually succeed in doing so was to find the means to love the dark side of ourselves—to find the reconciling understanding of our 'good-and-evil', afflicted human condition that was causing so much suffering and destruction!'[18]

These writers were right in identifying that what is inside us has implications on the world around us, although they would not necessarily see it as the result of rebelling against God. What

Christians would identify as sin—the grieving of God as we go against His loving laws—can only be dealt with by the saving grace provided in and through Jesus and then the transformation of our minds by the Holy Spirit.

We are reminded that: 'God cares about the earth, we are intimately connected with it and commanded to care for it, and God has promised to redeem it.'[19]

In Abraham Kuyper's famous dictum about God's sovereignty over the earth, there is the timely reminder: 'No piece of our mental world is to be hermetically sealed off from the rest, and there is not a square inch in the whole domain of our human existence over which Christ, who is Sovereign over all, does not cry: "Mine!"'[20]

Social

In treating our fellow human beings as being expendable in our pursuit for cheap food, we betray our fallacies and evidence our selfish ambitions in wanting more for the price of less. We belittle their labours and the impact it has on their health, lifestyles and communities. It relegates our estimate of them to being yet another commodity—a resource that we do not think about—which is opposite to the high regard in which God holds them. We have a disconnection between our food, the places where it has come from and the people who are affected.

There is a moral obligation that has thundered down from the eternal throne: we have a responsibility towards other people, especially those who are not able to defend themselves and are vulnerable to exploitation.

When an expert in the law asked Jesus 'Who is my neighbour?'

(Luke 10:29), it is still a relevant question for today. Indeed, it is more fitting, as we live in a global village. It is indicative of how real our faith is, as Jesus made clear in the parable of the sheep and the goats (Matthew 25:31–46). If we neglect to provide clothing, food and drink to those in positions of weakness, it shows that our faith is of minimal consequence to the way that we live.

We have to be honest and state that we live in a gluttonous society that depends on cheap products, which are sometimes low in nutrition and of low quality. We perpetrate social injustice as we demand low prices from farmers in our own country and elsewhere in the world. We are content to do this at the cost of the destruction of natural features, evidenced by the planting of plantations for palm oil in Indonesia, the deforestation of the Amazon so that more beef can be produced, and the dredging of the coral reefs so that we can eat fish in an unsustainable way. It flies in the opposite direction to the Biblical principle that we are to be stewards of creation.

Our perception is contrary to the attitude of God Himself who, in sending Jesus to die to save us from our sins, gave us His all because the price was worth it. And our response can still be self-centred: wanting the world to revolve around us when we should be focused on what God wants us to do with our lives and our attitudes. In short, He commands us to follow Him, to walk with Him and to obey His commands. It will be costly—both in time, money and lifestyle—but that is what true discipleship is all about.

As we have seen before, when Jesus said that the poor will always be among us, He was stating that the root cause of poverty is sin, including greed and gluttony (which is like idolatry). There is enough food in the world for everyone, yet there is still starvation in so many regions of the planet.

The statistics are staggering with 795 million people in the world not having enough food to live a healthy and active life. There are approximately 100 million people in developing countries who are underweight—that is one in six of humanity.

As usual, it is the youngest who suffer the most, as poor nutrition results in 45 per cent of children in the world dying before their fifth birthday—that is 3.1 million children per annum.

It is surely a travesty that, as 1 in 7 people do not get enough to eat, one-third of the food that is produced in thrown away.[21] Our luxurious lifestyles are literally causing the premature deaths of people in other parts of the world. We will be held responsible, for the Lord will say to us: 'Listen! Your brother's blood cries out to me from the ground' (Genesis 4:10). We must not and cannot take it lightly that the hardships in the world caused by low prices and hunger are a direct consequence of our wants and actions.

We are reminded continuously in the Bible of our responsibility towards those who are exploited by others and to treat them justly:

> But the needy will not always be forgotten, nor the hope of the afflicted ever perish (Psalm 9:18).

> Can a corrupt throne be allied with you—one that brings misery by its decrees? They band together against the righteous and condemn the innocent to death. But the LORD has become my fortress, and my God the rock in whom I take refuge. He will repay them for their sins and destroy them for their wickedness; the LORD our God will destroy them (Psalm 94:20–23).

Woe to those who make unjust laws, to those who issue oppressive decrees, to deprive the poor of their rights and withhold justice from the oppressed of my people, making widows their prey and robbing the fatherless. What will you do on the day of reckoning, when disaster comes from afar? To whom will you run for help? Where will you leave your riches? Nothing will remain but to cringe among the captives or fall among the slain. Yet for all this, his anger is not turned away, his hand is still upraised (Isaiah 10:1–4).

'Why have we fasted', they say, 'and you have not seen it? Why have we humbled ourselves, and you have not noticed?'

Yet on the day of your fasting, you do as you please and exploit all your workers. Your fasting ends in quarrelling and strife, and in striking each other with wicked fists. You cannot fast as you do today and expect your voice to be heard on high. Is it the kind of fast I have chosen, only a day for a man to humble himself? Is it only for bowing one's head like a reed and for lying on sackcloth and ashes? Is that what you call a fast, a day acceptable to the LORD?

Is not this the kind of fasting I have chosen: to loose the chains of injustice and untie the cords of the yoke, to set the oppressed free and break every yoke? Is it not to share your food with the hungry, and to provide the poor wanderer with shelter—when you see the naked, to clothe him, and not to turn away from your own flesh and blood? (Isaiah 58:3–7).

Among my people are wicked men who lie in wait like men who snare birds and like those who set traps to catch men.

Like cages full of birds, their houses are full of deceit; they have become rich and powerful and have grown fat and sleek. Their evil deeds have no limit; they do not plead the case of the fatherless to win it, they do not defend the rights of the poor.

'Should I not punish them for this?' declares the LORD. 'Should I not avenge myself on such a nation as this?'

A horrible and shocking thing has happened in the land. The

prophets prophesy lies, the priests rule by their own authority, and my people love it this way. But what will you do in the end? (Jeremiah 5:26–29).

'Woe to him who builds his palace by unrighteousness, his upper room by injustice, making his countryman work for nothing, not paying them for their labour. He says, "I will build myself a great palace with spacious upper rooms." So he makes large windows in it, panels it with cedar and decorates it in red.

'Does it make you a king to have more and more cedar? Did not your father have food and drink? He did what was right and just, so all went well with him. He defended the cause of the poor and needy, and so all went well. Is that not what it means to know me?' declares the LORD. 'But your eyes and your heart are set only on dishonest gain, on shedding innocent blood and on oppression and extortion' (Jeremiah 22:13–17).

You trample on the poor and force him to give you grain. Therefore, though you have built stone mansions, you will not live in them; though you have planted lush vineyards, you will not drink their wine.

For I know how many are your offences and how great your sins. You oppress the righteous and take bribes, and you deprive the poor of justice in the courts (Amos 5:11–12).

Hear this, you who trample the needy and do away with the poor of the land, saying, 'When will the New Moon be over that we may sell grain, and the Sabbath will be ended that we may market wheat?'— skimping the measure, boosting the price and cheating with dishonest scales, buying the poor with silver and the needy for a pair of sandals, selling even the sweepings with wheat.

The LORD has sworn by the Pride of Jacob, 'I will never forget anything they have done' (Amos 8:4–7).

Our attitude should be reflected in the words of Micah 6:8: 'He has showed you, O man, what is good. And what does the Lord require of you? To act justly and to love mercy and to walk humbly with your God.'

If these were not enough, the psalmist reminds us:

> Blessed is the man who fears the Lord, who finds great delight his commands...
>
> Wealth and riches are in his house, and his righteousness endures for ever. Even in darkness light dawns for the upright, for the gracious and compassionate and righteous man. Good will come to him who is generous and lends freely, who conducts his affairs with justice. Surely he will never be shaken; a righteous man will be remembered for ever...
>
> He has scattered abroad his gifts to the poor, his righteousness endures for ever, his horn [i.e. his dignity] will be lifted high in honour (Psalm 112:1, 3–6, 9).

It is said of the wife of noble character: 'She opens her arms to the poor and extends her hands to the needy' (Proverbs 31:20).

This is what the Lord Almighty says: 'Administer true justice, show mercy and compassion to one another. Do not oppress the widow or the fatherless, the alien or the poor. In your hearts do not think evil of each other' (Zechariah 7:9–10).

We need to have the conviction that we are not to exploit the poor, however far away they may be from us geographically. God still wants them to be close to our hearts as they are to His,

We need to examine our own hearts and even walk past those stores that sell food produced as a result of human exploitation. Just because it is cheap does not make it right. We cannot argue that we are saving money so that we can give it to the Lord. He has thundered in His word that our worship is pointless unless we obey Him (1 Samuel 15:22–23), and that includes caring for our neighbour in our global village.

We need to be courageous, caring for the concerns of people made in the image of God who have been exploited for the sake of cheap foodstuffs.

ACTION POINTS

- *Be more aware of where your food comes from.*
- *Buy fewer ready-made sandwiches and meals.*
- *Avoid processed, convenience and fast foods.*
- *Eat less red meat so you can contribute to less CO2 emissions.*
- *Search for more information about the disadvantaged and oppressed people (e.g. by contacting Tearfund, World Vision).*

NOTES

1 '"Rampant consumerism" criticised', *BBC News*, 5 June 2008, http://news.bbc.co.uk/1/hi/uk/7436704.stm

2 Kent Carlson and Michael Lueken, *Renovation of the Church: What happens when a seeker church discovers spiritual formation*, (Downers Grove, Illinois: Inter Varsity Press, 2011), p. 35

3 Rick Stearns, *The Hole in Our Gospel* (Nashville, Tennessee: Thomas Nelson Inc, 2009), p. 122

4 Quoted in: Ross Kaminsky, 'Reading and Rereading the Wondrous Peggy Noonan', *The Spectator*, 5 November 2015, https://spectator.org/64567_reading-and-rereading-wondrous-peggy-noonan/

5 Rick Stearns, *The Hole in Our Gospel* (Nashville, Tennessee: Thomas Nelson Inc, 2009), p. 216

6 Aisha Majid and Sarah Newey, 'Defusing the "demographic timebomb":

the world's population challenges in 13 charts', *Daily Telegraph*, 18 September 2018, https://www.telegraph.co.uk/news/0/defusing-demographic-timebomb-worlds-population-challenges-13/

7   Sarah Newey, 'Give up meat completely or become a "flexitarian" to save the planet, say experts', *Daily Telegraph*, 10 October 2018, https://www.telegraph.co.uk/news/0/give-meat-completely-become-flexitarian-save-planet-say-experts/

8   United Nations News Centre, 'UN urges food sector to reduce fossil fuel and shift to "energy-smart agriculture"', 30 November 2011 http://www.un.org/apps/news/story.asp?NewsID=40579#.WmnJg6hl_IU

9   Tara Garnett, 'Food and Climate Change: The world on a plate', Food Climate Research Network, https://fcrn.org.uk/sites/default/files/FCRN_Generic.ppt; for a more startling analysis, see: P J Gerber et al, *Tackling climate change through livestock—A global assessment of emissions and mitigation opportunities* (Rome: Food and Agriculture Organisation of the United Nations (FAO), 2013), http://www.fao.org/docrep/018/i3437e/i3437e.pdf

10 Cited in: Sarah Newey, 'Give up meat completely or become a "flexitarian" to save the planet, say experts', *Daily Telegraph*, 10 October 2018, https://www.telegraph.co.uk/news/0/give-meat-completely-become-flexitarian-save-planet-say-experts/

11 Ibid.

12 Chris Mooney, 'Scientists may have found a solution to the atmosphere's methane mystery', *Washington Post*, 29 September 2017, https://www.washingtonpost.com/gdpr-consent/?destination=%2fnews%2fenergy-environment%2fwp%2f2017%2f09%2f29%2fscientists-find-that-belching-cows-could-solve-a-key-mystery-about-the-atmosphere%2f%3f&utm_term=.c91021acfa30

13 Lucas Reijnders and Sam Soret, 'Quantification of the environmental impact of different dietary protein choices', *The American Journal of Clinical Nutrition*, 78 (3), September 2003, 6645–6685, https://academic.oup.com/ajcn/article/78/3/664S/4690011

14 'Amazon rainforest deforestation "worst in 10 years", says Brazil', *BBC News*, 24 November 2018, https://www.bbc.co.uk/news/world-latin-

america-46327634

15 Pascale Palmer, 'Hungry for Change', *Bible in Transmission*, Bible Society, Summer 2013, p. 23

16 Namy Espinoza-Orias and Adisa Azapagic, 'Understanding the impact on climate change of convenience food: Carbon footprint of sandwiches', *Journal of Sustainable Production and Consumption*, volume 15, July 2018, pp. 1–15, https://www.sciencedirect.com/science/article/abs/pii/S2352550917300635?via%3Dihub

17 Lauren van der Post, *A Walk with a White Bushman* (New York: Random House, 1986), p. 112

18 Jeremy Griffith, *The Real Book of Answers to Everything* (NSW, Australia: WTM Publishing and Communications Pty Ltd, 2011) p. 103, pdf can be obtained through https://www.humancondition.com/human-condition/

19 Jason Fletcher, 'Because...', *World Vision magazine*, Summer 2007, www.worlddvision.org.uk/church

20 Abraham Kuyper, 'Sphere Sovereignty', in: James D Bratt, *Abraham Kuyper: A Centennial Reader* (Grand Rapids: Wm B Eardman, 1998), p.461

21 Food Aid Foundation, 'Hunger Statistics', http://www.foodaidfoundation.org/world-hunger-statistics.html

13 Spiritual

Teach me, O Lord, to follow your decrees; then I will keep them to the end. Give me understanding, and I will keep your law and obey it with all my heart (Psalm 119:33–34).

Whatever is true, whatever is noble, whatever is right, whatever is pure, whatever is lovely, whatever is admirable—if anything is excellent or praiseworthy—think about such things ... put it into practice. And the God of peace will be with you (Philippians 4:8–9).

The dangers

There is the danger that we can view food as the be all and end all. Conversely, the same danger can be found on the other end of the spectrum where food is avoided, and the body image is all that matters. We need to get a balance between misusing and deifying the body—the solution is one that only Jesus can provide for He wants us to look at ourselves from His eternal viewpoint.

On the one hand, we can take a similar approach to the ancient Greeks, thinking that the body is only useful because it carries the soul, which is regarded as the most important part.

In adopting this approach, we neglect the point that God created us to be holistic—one entity made up of several parts. He created Adam with the body before breath was given to the man (Genesis 2:7). After the Fall, the effects of sin were seen both bodily (through death) and spiritually (with separation from God).

Indeed, we are commanded to love God with our whole being—heart (physical), soul and strength (Deuteronomy 6:5).

Jesus thought that the body was so important that He came in flesh as a baby. After His death and resurrection, He was seen in bodily form, as evidenced by His eating of breakfast (John 21:1–14).

We are told that, at the end of time, we will be given new bodies (1 Corinthians 15:44) and not float around as ethereal spirits.

On the other hand, we can fall into the opposite realm of esteeming our bodies too much, as we have seen throughout this book. We can turn it into a god instead of dedicating it to God.

Impact of sin

It has been discovered that people who are religious are less likely to experience eating disorders.[1] However, it should not draw us into complacency but to look out lest we fall into that sin after being tempted (1 Corinthians 10:12). If we are not overweight or obese, it is only by the grace of God. However, in looking at the average congregation, it is fair to say that this sin has already infiltrated the Church.

We can often smugly regard the sins mentioned in Romans chapter 1 as not applying to Christians, but, if we look closely, we will see the sin of greed mentioned among those deserving judgement. The good news is that it is also mentioned among those sins that are covered by the grace of God; the mercy that can remove all the common conditions of humanity that keep us separated from God. The gospel tells us that we '...were washed, you were sanctified, you were justified in the name of the Lord Jesus Christ and by the Spirit of our God' (1 Corinthians 6:11).

We must stop saying that we are Christians but continue to live as though God does not mean much to us, preferring to be like the world around us. It is as though we are content to accept Jesus as Saviour but denying His right to be our Lord—so we are effectively living a double life.

Within the Church, there is a tendency to rate sins, but God says that sin is sin is sin—no distinctions, no excuses. We often dress gaining weight as problems, syndromes or conditions, but it really is rebellion against our Creator. The stark reality is that sin is saying, 'Shove off God, I'm in charge. No to your rules.' However nicely we dress it up, it is precisely what we are saying to God when we would rather overindulge on unhealthy foods than follow what He has instructed. He demands wholehearted obedience, as demonstrated in the words of Joshua: '... as for me and my household, we will serve the LORD' (Joshua 24:15).

When we overindulge, we replicate the sin of Adam and Eve (Genesis chapter 3) in saying that, despite the sumptuousness and delights that God has given to us, we still want more. God is so amazing, as we are reminded—'He has shown kindness by giving you rain from heaven and crops in their seasons; he provides you with plenty of food and fills your hearts with joy' (Acts 14:17). The more we demand of what we want, there is an increasing likelihood that the consequences will be disastrous. The food mountain that we consume builds up a wall between us and God.

We tend to think that it is a problem for other people. In an article titled 'The Socially Acceptable Sin', Jason Todd has written: 'When I think of gluttony, I think about my desire to shove a dozen donuts into my mouth and wash them down with chocolate milk. Or perhaps it's my tendency to mindlessly feed chips to a stomach that's no longer hungry. Many of us look at the sin of gluttony and think, "That's not really my struggle". Or we think, "What's the big deal?" After all, most congregations have compulsive overeaters among them, and they're not considered "less spiritual" or "backsliders" for it.'[2]

Solomon gives a stern warning: 'Listen, my son, and be wise, and keep your heart on the right path. Do not join with those who drink too much wine or gorge themselves on meat, for drunkards and gluttons become poor, and drowsiness clothes them in rags' (Proverbs 23:19–21).

We can dress it up as much as we like, but there is no getting away from the fact that it is an afront to God, as we abuse our bodies and misuse the resources that He has given to us. This attempted softening of our condemnation is illustrated by a cartoon displaying a sign in front of a café: 'Specialising in meals that leave you bloated and lethargic, followed by self-loathing.' It depicts a man saying to his wife: 'I liked it better when they called it comfort food.'[3]

It is the mentality of worldliness that has entered the Church when we cry out 'Give! Give!' (Proverbs 30:15) and never realise that, in Christ, we have all that is enough. We do not need another sugar rush, but a greater filling of the Holy Spirit.

There is levity in the pews when a church leader stands up and confesses his or her indulgence for cheesecake or propensity for seconds or thirds. But there is less laxity if that same church leader was to confess to taking cocaine or claiming state benefits for which they were not entitled so depriving widows and orphans. However, in God's eyes, there is no difference. The truth is that many church ministers, who conduct the funerals of people in their congregation, may find others officiating at their funeral due to a premature death caused by obesity and an unhealthy lifestyle.

It is a problem when leaders of the church may be the biggest culprits.[4] The New Testament warns us that, if we want to be teachers (and this is from the youngest to the oldest person), we need to aim to keep our whole body in check (James 3:1–2). It is not just the words that come out of our mouths that speak to people, but also the inches around our waistline. It is impossible to speak of Jesus Christ as being the Lord of all, when we have declined to give Him authority over our appetite and our spending on fast food, demonstrated by the neglect of our body.

If someone brought a pornographic magazine into one of our fellowship meetings or stole from the collection, we would be rightly affronted, as we see it going against what God has commanded. Yet we do not see the double standards in allowing unhealthy food being brought into fellowship meals, especially where we have the duty to look after the children in our churches and not bring harm upon them. We see how seriously God takes it when He shouts out: 'Their destiny is destruction, their god is their stomach, and their glory is in their shame. Their mind is on earthly things' (Philippians 3:19). If that is how people behave who do not have a relationship with Jesus, how much more different should children of the King act! Jesus re-emphasised the point when He stated: 'Watch out! Be on your guard against all kinds of greed; a man's life does not consist in the abundance of his possessions' (Luke 12:15.

Shannon McCoy has commented:

Perhaps you don't believe that overeating is a sin. Many of us have been brainwashed by magazine articles, television talk shows, and reality shows that tell us food is the problem: you are simply eating the wrong things in the wrong way. Often even the Christian perspective views overeating as a diet problem rather than a sin problem. On the other hand, you may know that overeating is a sin, but it does not seem serious because it is often treated as one of those little sins that are acceptable in the church. You don't hear sermons or read books on the sin of overeating. Your focus is more on getting treatment for your problem of overeating than facing up to your personal responsibility of repentance and obedience. According to the above descriptions of sin, overeating is of folly, not of faith. It is failing to do the right thing. It is unrighteousness and lawlessness.[5]

We have allowed so-called 'ancient' heresies into our churches. When John wrote against the Gnostic teachings in the first century AD, I am sure he would be horrified that we have since welcomed them with open arms. One of their tenets was that the body was purely of this world and is of no consequence, being 'contemptable, being a development of Plato's division of body, intellect and spirit'. It did not have any intrinsic value of itself and imprisoned the true self—the so-called 'precious' spirit within.[6] There was a hierarchy as the 'inner body' was more real and more important than the body itself. The eventual outcome was it did not matter what happened to the body and so it could be abused.[7] Although Christians may not intellectually assent to this doctrine, their lives can clearly demonstrate the self-harm that they inflict on their bodies by gluttony and idleness.

Flaccid Christians are the opposite of how God wants us to be and, indeed, such portrayals are a hinderance to the Christian life that should be demonstrated to a watching world. Middle-age spread is not a badge of honour for it shows that we are living incorrectly—contrary to how God wants us to be. If we claim that Jesus is Lord of our lives, we should be different and 'abstain from sinful desires' (1 Peter 2:11).

Where we should be showing distinctiveness, we are assimilating into the world's way of thinking. Where we should be leading the way in healthy living, we are following with stocky waistlines. Jesus commanded us to show others the way of His Kingly reign:

> You are the salt of the earth. But if the salt loses its saltiness, how can it be made salty again? It is no longer good for anything, except to be thrown out and trampled by men.

> You are the light of the world. A city on a hill cannot be hidden. Neither do people light a lamp and put it under a bowl. Instead, they put it on its stand, and it gives light to everyone in the house. In the same way, let your light shine before men, that they may see your good deeds and praise your Father in heaven. (Matthew 5:13–16).

People will think that we are different if we live according to God's way of living—not when we are selfishly satisfying our own appetites without regard for God, others or even our own needs.

We are urged to be blameless and pure so that we '... shine like stars in the universe' (Philippians 2:15). We cannot be showing that we are walking closely with God if we are waddling in the ways of the world.

When Jesus calls us to follow Him (Matthew 4:19; 16:24), He tells us that it will be costly. We will have to give up our hedonistic lifestyle and submit to His way of life. It means giving up on our overflowing freezers and fridges, and turning our minds to how God wants us to live—sacrificially, heavenward and serving both our heavenly Father and the people He created.

We should be thinking and behaving according to God's Kingdom principles, putting evil desires to death. Although we are not to treat it literally, we are instructed to '... put a knife to your throat if you are given to gluttony' (Proverbs 23:2). It could be the ancient version of the gastric band!

As Tim Keller reminds us: 'Everything that troubles [us] is a result of idolatry. And what is idolatry? It's taking a good thing and making it an ultimate thing.'[8]

God thinks it so important that He gave a commandment about it: 'You shall have no other gods before me' (Exodus 20:3). It is not that God has pre-eminence over other gods, as the meaning is deeper than that. The original Hebrew means that there are to be no other gods 'before my face'—that is God does not want other idols even in His presence. We may think that we do not have idols in the old-fashioned sense like wooden- or stone-carved images. We may even think that we have not succumbed to the modern equivalents like worshipping our cars, careers or even our families. However, the ever stretching of the measuring tape around our torso will indicate that our creature comforts, like the luscious cream cakes or the mega-sized pizza, would take priority over what God has ordained for us. Sin is precisely what is happening when we defy what He has commanded us to do in looking after the bodies He has given us.

In case we think that idolatry was a phenomenon that only happened in ancient cultures, Kevin DeYoung reminds us that there were certain characteristics that are still around today: 'The whole system of idolatry—guaranteed, selfish, easy, convenient, normal, logical, pleasing, indulgent, and erotic—when you look at it that way, the allure of idolatry does not seem far removed from us.'[9]

Indeed, John Calvin defined idolatry as worshipping 'the gifts in place of the giver himself'.[10] It is a challenge to our mindsets. Our claim that Jesus is Lord of all is not demonstrated in our inability to refrain from having another unhealthy snack.

It is not only a challenge to our waistline but also to our pockets. It has been stated that Jesus talked more about money, possessions and time (about 15 per cent of the teaching), than He spent on instruction about heaven and hell. How we spend our money is a great indicator of where our priorities are. Jesus reminded us in the Sermon on the Mount: 'For where your treasure is, there your heart will be also' (Matthew 6:21). How can we say that we have the Kingdom of God as our priority when our personal food bill is substantially more than we give to God's work through the local church and other Christian agencies?

We may be storing up our 'treasures on earth' (Matthew 6:19), as the fat accumulates around our waist and so, be depriving God of our money and our lifespan as we purposely shorten it by diabetes, strokes and heart disease because we do not seek for God take control over all of our life. We face a stark choice as Jesus declared that we cannot serve God and possessions (Matthew 6:24). We need to bow our knees before Him and confess that He has not always been the Lord of everything, asking Him to rule over our whole beings including our stomachs, our dietary choices and our lifestyles.

The bad news is that there are consequences if we place the idol of gluttony at the centre of our lives for it can shorten our lifespan and will make us less productive for God's Kingdom. This outcome includes the financial aspect, as our money will be tied up in purchasing unhealthy food rather than towards blessing other people.

However, the good news is that God does promise thriving in the spiritual sense for those who obey His commands, as they seek to give everything to Him, including their bodies. If we resist the temptation to overindulge and so become overweight/obese as a consequence, God does give us promises:

> If they obey and serve Him, they will spend the rest of their days in prosperity and their years in contentment (Job 36:11).

> My son, do not forget my teaching, but keep my commands in your heart, for they will prolong your life many years, and bring you prosperity (Proverbs 3:1–2).

> He who obeys instruction guards his life, but he who is contemptuous of his ways will die (Proverbs 19:16).

The overindulgence in food and the sedentary lifestyle is convenient with fast-food outlets and convenience stores. We have now become used to the idea of ordering unhealthy food, by mobile phone or laptops, to our doors without us even having to stand up. It has the allure of receiving much without having to do anything or very little—it is part of our culture that thinks it is all about me and my wants. The easy purchase of these goods feels safe because we know that up and down our nations, there are thousands and millions of people who are doing exactly what we are doing in order to get a quick fix for our cravings. Our senses are easily satisfied in plastic containers or paper bags filled with substances that are not nutritionally good for us and will give us long-term consequences, that we may deal with for the rest of our lives.

We need to heed the exhortation from John: 'Dear children, keep yourselves from idols' (1 John 5:21). The apostle is not merely referring to fast cars and other items that we term 'materialistic', but also those things that we cannot see—mainly because we put them so fast into our mouths! We abuse food, the growers and the earth that produced it because, as we were reminded, we make it the ultimate, placing desire for gratification over our gratification for God.

How we look after our bodies is part of our witness to others. We are reminded that we are to 'love your neighbours as yourself' (Mark 12:31), often neglecting the part that we are to love ourselves— body, spirit, mind—because God has created us for His glory. If we neglect to look after that which He has entrusted to us, it says much about how we regard God and, in turn, it reflects our attitude to others.

If we do not look after the body that God has given to us then we cannot help others. We cannot do the good works to which He has called us because we are physically unfit and so unable to complete them; we will not reach out to our community through voluntary work as we will be laid down by the avoidable conditions brought on by being overweight or obese; we will not be able to contribute to our bank account, to the needs of our family, to society by means of taxes (indeed, we could drain resources be receiving benefits) and to God's work because we are unable to work due to the effects of obesity.

There is another aspect to this in that how we treat our bodies is how we regard the esteem of others. The message we are giving to friends, family and especially our spouses if we 'go to seed' is that we do not care much for their opinions and regard. We should seek to be in the best possible health not for narcissistic reasons, but so that they can benefit.

For example, in the marriage vows, we say: 'my body I give to you'. It says much if the body we are giving to them is unhealthy, overweight and creaking because of neglect and mismanagement. It also speaks to our culture that Christians care little about working at relationships, especially with husbands or wives, because of the way we treat ourselves.

We should heed the warning as obesity is not a new problem, for, in the Bible, there are two instances where being obese was the cause of death or a contributory factor. One was Eglon, the king of Moab (Judges 3:12–30). The other was Eli the high priest (1 Samuel 4:12–22), whose obesity caused him to fall off his chair and break his neck at the hearing of bad news—the Bible described him as being 'an old man and heavy' (v.18).

We are urged not to give into greed:

> So I say, live by the Spirit, and you will not gratify the desires of the sinful nature (Galatians 5:16).

> Put to death, therefore, whatever belongs to your earthly nature ... evil desires and greed, which is idolatry (Colossians 3:5).

We are told repeatedly that, if we are Christians, we are to look after our bodies as the Holy Spirit is inside us. We are reminded by Paul:

> Don't you know that you yourselves are God's temple and that God's Spirit lives in you? If anyone destroys God's temple, God will destroy him; for God's temple is sacred, and you are that temple (1 Corinthians 3:16–17).

> Do you not know that your body is a temple of the Holy Spirit, who is in you, whom you have received from God? You are not your own; you were bought at a price. Therefore, honour God with your body (1 Corinthians 6:19–20).

> What agreement is there between the temple of God and idols? For we are the temple of the living God. As God has said: 'I will live with them and walk among them, and I will be their God, and they will be my people.'[11]

It is followed by an injunction and a promise:

> 'Therefore, come out from them and be separate', says the Lord. 'Touch no unclean thing, and I will receive you.[12] I will be a Father to you, and you will be my sons and daughters', says the Lord Almighty.[13] (2 Corinthians 6:16–18).

There should be no dichotomy between our words and our actions if we have acknowledged Jesus Christ as being in charge of our lives. It has been calculated that Jesus is referred to as 'Lord' more times than as 'Saviour'. However, we often deny that truth by saying: 'No, Lord'—a contradiction between our deeds and our declaration. We can be tempted to dampen the prompt to leave the way that we should have left behind—when we should have had our minds renewed by the Holy Spirit and had futile thinking removed from our mindset:

> They are darkened in their understanding and separated from the life of God because of the ignorance that is in them due to the hardening of their hearts. Having lost all sensitivity, they have given themselves over to sensuality so as to indulge in every kind of impurity, with a continual lust for more (Ephesians 4:18–19).

There is the encouragement that we should be treating our bodies in new ways, as the epistle continues:

> You, however, did not come to know Christ in that way. Surely you heard of him and were taught in him in accordance with the truth that is in Jesus. You were taught, with regard to your former way of life, to put off your old self, which is being corrupted by its deceitful desires; to be made new in the attitude of your minds; and to put on the new self, created to be like God in true righteousness and holiness (Ephesians 4:20–24).

Jesus calls us emphatically to take up our cross and follow Him (Luke 9:23). We cannot do that if we are so full up with our desire for food (literally) and our lack of fitness that we cannot follow Him effectively. The call is not an option but a command to forsake all that will get in the way of wholeheartedly following God, including unhealthy lifestyles which do not glorify Him. We often show our lack of trust in Him for our daily bread (Matthew 6:11), because we want to demonstrate our self-sufficiency by overindulging in food.

C S Lewis has commented that, 'Nearly all that we call history ... [is] the long terrible story of man trying to find something other than God which will make him happy.'[14] Even in our pews, we would prefer to have our idol of gluttony satisfied even while we are supposedly offering up our worship to God.

In this way, Christians can often live like atheists by being so centred on worldly pleasures (in this instance, the desire for unhealthy lifestyles) that they miss out on the best way that God wants us to live.

When we remove the mindset that is based on burgers and biscuits, pizzas and pastries, and replace it with wholesome thoughts, then we will find the new life so very satisfying—more so than any milkshake or soda. Our brains should be filled with: '...whatever is true, whatever is noble, whatever is right, whatever is pure, whatever is lovely, whatever is admirable—if anything is excellent or praiseworthy—think about such things' (Philippians 4:8).

John Piper commented: 'Gluttony is having a craving for food that conquers you', before adding: 'The main way to fight cravings, that we don't want, is to experience higher cravings and have them master us.'[15]

The good news is that we are to be supporters of each other as we seek to live lives that are God-honouring in all ways, including how we are stewards of the bodies that God has given to us. We are exhorted to: '... put off falsehood and speak truthfully to his neighbour, for we are all members of one body' (Ephesians 4:25). There is nothing like the power of being supported in prayer, so there is three people involved: the person with the sin of obesity; the one walking with them; and God Himself. For, as we confess our sins to each other and pray for one another, then there is healing (James 5:16).

It does not matter if we do not have a problem with being

overweight or obese, we must walk with those who find the lure of chocolate (or any other failings) a constant and real temptation. There is no room in the Church for super-spirituality for we may find ourselves in that situation one day and we have to acknowledge that there may be other pits that we may fall into. 'So, if you think you are standing firm, be careful that you don't fall!' (1 Corinthians 10:12). The Scripture is not one of pessimism for, as we walk past the temptations of overeating or eating the wrong things, we are given the promise: 'No temptation has seized you except what is common to man. And God is faithful; he will not let you be tempted beyond what you can bear. But when you are tempted, he will also provide a way out so that you can stand up under it' (1 Corinthians 10:13).

One means of providing an exit is by conviction of the Holy Spirit. Another means is by the church community as we are to be promoters of healthy lifestyles and encourage others to do so as well:

> We who are strong ought to bear with the failings of the weak and not to please ourselves. Each of us should please his neighbour for his good, to build him up. For even Christ did not please himself but, as it is written: 'The insults of those who insult you have fallen on me.'[16] For everything that was written in the past was written to teach us, so that through endurance and the encouragement of the Scriptures we might have hope.
>
> May the God who gives endurance and encouragement give you a spirit of unity among yourselves as you follow Christ Jesus, so that with one heart and mouth you may glorify the God and Father of our Lord Jesus Christ (Romans 15:1–6).

Furthermore, we do not just have an obligation to encourage those in the church to follow a healthy lifestyle, but also those who are not in it. Indeed, Paul reminds us that this concern is a distinguishing mark of the gospel that we are changed holistically, being aware that God has created all of us, not just the spirit. It is a mark of reaching out to all around to state that Jesus wants to be the Lord of all of our life, just as He laid down His own life on the cross. He died to remove all of our sins—such is sin that it is not distinguishable, for the sin of gluttony, covetousness and idolatry are as abhorrent to God as those of murder, lying and the misuse of the gift of sex. In effect, our promotion of healthy living demonstrates God's love for us, so that we can share this good news to our neighbours and to all in our communities.

> So whether you eat or drink or whatever you do, do it all for the glory of God. Do not cause anyone to stumble, whether Jews, Greeks or the church of God—even as I try to please everybody in every way. For I am not seeking my own good but the good of many, so that they may be saved. Follow my example, as I follow the example of Christ (1 Corinthians 10:31–11:1).

It is noticeable that God does give us the strength and vision of how He can use our bodies, but He chooses other Christians to walk with us so that we would honour and please Him in all that we do. It is important to note that the primary aim is not to have a healthy lifestyle with proper eating and regular exercise, although these are important, but to worship God through our bodies, in all ways. Paul urges us, '... in view of God's mercy, to offer your bodies as living sacrifices, holy and pleasing to God—this is your spiritual act of worship' (Romans 12:1).

God is not a killjoy, but He delights in us when we use our bodies properly, which brings glory to Him. David Platt has usefully reminded us (although the context is sexual morality, the truth is also applicable about other aspects of healthy living):

> Not only are our bodies designed for God, but God is devoted to our bodies. Literally, he is for your body. God wants you to experience the maximum joy for which your body is built, and as the Creator of our bodies, he knows what will bring them the most pleasure. This takes us back to one of the core truths of the gospel—the reality that God loves us and is for us, not against us. God desires the best for us, and he has designed our bodies not just for his glory but also for our good.
>
> This is why God, in his love, gives us boundaries for our bodies: he loves us and knows what is best for us. He desires to protect us from harm and provide for us something greater than we can see. Whenever God gives us a negative command, he always gives two positives to us: he is providing us with something better while also protecting us from something worse ...
>
> These simple truths help us see more clearly what we are doing when we ignore God's good instructions. All throughout the Bible he gives us instructions for how our bodies are to be used. But when we ignore these instructions, it's as if we're saying to God, "You don't know how this body is to be used. I know better than you do." It seems a bit arrogant, doesn't it?[17]

Although there may be good intentions (like New Year's resolutions, lying in tatters after a few months), there is nothing like seeking God and asking Him to change our mindset, which is the seat of all our behaviours. We hear the injunction: 'Do not conform any longer to the pattern of this world, but be transformed by the renewing of your mind. Then you will be able to test and approve what God's will is—his good, pleasing and perfect will' (Romans 12:2).

The Old Testament also has the cry to God that our mindsets would be radically changed so that we walk in His ways: 'Create in me a pure heart, O God, and renew a steadfast spirit within me' (Psalm 51:10).

When we want to follow God with all of our being, He will give us that vision of how He wants us to live, especially as he created us. He has not left us with silence, but His Word instructs us clearly in the way we should go. It is a common and true parlance that the Bible is 'the Best Information Before Life Ends'. When we have our minds so renewed, we will know the truth: 'Submit yourselves, then, to God. Resist the devil, and he will flee from you' (James 4:7). If we live like this, we will know the freedom of living life in abundance (John 10:10) and not being enslaved to our carnal nature.

If we continue to live how we want to, overindulging and neglecting physical activity, there will be consequences as has been outlined elsewhere. There will be disorders and outcomes that will affect ourselves and others, but we will also rob ourselves of the peace that God gives. He wants us to be pleased with what He has given to us, for He created it to be very good (Genesis 1:31).

We have yet to grasp what a wonderful thing our bodies are, for King David reminds us: 'I praise you because I am fearfully and wonderfully made; your works are wonderful, I know that full well' (Psalm 139:14). There is a great truth in the saying: 'God does not make rubbish'.

J Scott McElroy wrote that: 'my body, a temple of the Holy Spirit and container of my spirit, is to be maintained and "stewarded" in a way that will maximise its use as an instrument for God. Though it is dust, it's a glorious feat of engineering and work of art (though imperfect) and offers me the opportunity to do things in this world that can only be done while inhabiting this body.'[18]

Despite the fact that we might have the life of Christ in us, we can still live a lie—a life that is still conforming to what is contrary to how God wants us to live:

> Those who live according to the sinful nature have their minds set on what that nature desires; but those who live in accordance with the Spirit have their minds set on what the Spirit desires. The mind of sinful man is death, but the mind controlled by the Spirit is life and peace; the sinful mind is hostile to God. It does not submit to God's law, nor can it do so. Those controlled by the sinful nature cannot please God (Romans 8:5–8).

The tragedy is that, because we often want our own way, as manifested by our relationship with our bodies, it will deprive us of a wholesome life on earth, but, more importantly, it will be severely detrimental to our relationship with God. If our minds are so full of thoughts about food, it will limit the space in our brains to think about Him. We will end up looking like everybody else, appearing as though we have not submitted our lives to God and looking like experts in greed instead (2 Peter 2:13)—which will not reflect our heavenly Father to those people that we come into contact with. If our minds are not fully concerned about Him, there is the ironic prospect of being limited in the blessings that He wants to bestow upon us. We are unable to honour God because our minds are on the next servings of hamburgers or hummus.

We can find ourselves in debt as we put more emphasis on food. In doing so, we deprive God of other ways of worship, such as bringing Him our tithes. As the pounds pile up, so can the credit bills—all because we want to indulge in gluttony. It is stopping us bringing all of ourselves and what God has given to us as stewards, and we dishonour Him by not doing so.

As is usual, God is ahead of the science that we are discovering, for humanity is only now proving what God's Word has been saying—to live a full life, we need to follow the instructions that God has already evidently given to us.

As followers of the Master, we must have a different perspective on the temporal—accepting that all good things come from God but realising that we can have the same sinful viewpoint as people who do not know Him and think that the resources around us are for our pleasure alone.

> Do not love the world or anything in the world. If anyone loves the world, the love of the Father is not in him. For everything in the world—the cravings of sinful man, the lust of his eyes and the boasting of what he has and does—comes not from the Father but from the world. The world and its desires pass away, but the man who does the will of God lives for ever (1 John 2:15–17).

The Greek word used in that passage is 'epithumeō', which literally means 'over desires'—the turning of the created good things into the sole or prevailing goal of our lives.

There can be an obsession with food as people live from meal to meal, counting the minutes and seconds before they can consume again. The look at the cream cake (or whatever your particular culinary temptation is) will infiltrate your mind, before you boast to others about how you succumbed to that specific sin. It might not even be a physical boast, but the expanding girth will give away that you have not sought God to treat His creation with the respect that it is due. Our obsession with the temporal is given away by the bragging of what is in our larder/freezer/any other place that you store food. It might not be the excessive hording of tins but can be exhibited by the proclamation of how many Easter eggs we have received or any other food.

You eat what you become, as Moses reminded the Israelites: 'He humbled you, causing you to hunger and then feeding you with manna, which neither you nor your fathers had known, to teach you that man does not live on bread alone but on every word that comes from the mouth of the Lord' (Deuteronomy 8:3). This verse was quoted by Jesus to Satan in Matthew 4:4 during the specific time of temptations after Jesus' baptism and fasting in the wilderness. This affirmation is that there is a deeper life than physical hunger, as was demonstrated in the following verse: 'Know then in your heart that as a man disciplines his son, so the Lord your God disciplines you' (Deuteronomy 8:5). God knows that we are not just spiritual but holistic. We are not only physical beings but we are to be aware that knowing God is greater than any gateaux or gammon steak could be.

This realisation is expressed in the prayer of the apostle Paul for the Church (and that includes us): 'May your whole spirit, soul and *body* be kept blameless at the coming of our Lord Jesus Christ' (1 Thessalonians 5:23) [my emphasis].

As we are created to live full and fulfilling lives, let us be aware of the consumption of greed, which will then deprive us of living how God wants us to. He wants us to develop into being the humans that He created us to be. An example of this is that He wants us to develop the fruits of the Spirit (Galatians 5:22–23) as proof that He is living within us, one of which is self-control. When we want to consciously make that decision to follow what God instructs, He has given 'great and precious promises' with the result that 'through them you may participate in the divine nature and escape the corruption in the world caused by evil desires' (2 Peter 1:4).

One of the consequences of relying on His divine power is, once again, that we will develop self-control (2 Peter 1:6), and so the virtuous circle of godly behaviour is established. How can we show that we are earnest followers of Jesus when we are binge-watching television while gorging ourselves with junk food? God wants us to wake up and realise that this is not the way of discipleship, but Satan's means of distracting us and ineffective in the ways of the Kingdom. An overweight or obese Christian is a bad advertisement as to how a Christian should live life. We must be able to say 'No!' to excess and say 'Yes!' to Jesus.

When the scales are tipped in the wrong way, there is more that we need to do than eat healthily and undertake physical exercise, as we have to confess that we have grieved God and ask for forgiveness. There is a way back from being obese or overweight, apart from the physical and psychological efforts, for John gives us the comforting words: 'If we confess our sins, he is faithful and just and will forgive us our sins and purify us from all unrighteousness' (1 John 1:9).

Above all, it tells much to society around us if we care little enough for our body, even though Jesus came and died for all of us, and the Holy Spirit wants to live in us as His temple. We need to be so full of Jesus that other temptations cannot get a foothold, being satisfied with our lives that God has given us and the Saviour with whom we will be living eternally. We are exhorted not to get drunk on wine, but to be filled with the Holy Spirit instead (Ephesians 5:18). Everything else, including the craving to make food king above all else, will melt away, so we can say with the Old Testament writer: 'I thought in my heart, "Come now, I will test you with pleasure to find out what is good." But that also proved to be meaningless' (Ecclesiastes 2:1).

The same author points us back to the fact that God is the Creator of all that use and consume: 'For without him, who can eat or find enjoyment?' (Ecclesiastes 2:25). Paul reminds us that, '... godliness with contentment is great gain. For we brought nothing into the world, and we can take nothing out of it. But if we have food and clothing, we will be content with that' (1 Timothy 6:6–8).

The Bible often uses the image of the body as referring to those who are following Jesus as Lord and Saviour[19], in the same way that the Church is described as the bride of Christ.[20] We should be looking forward to the day to come when the Lord 'will banish the names of the idols from the land, and they will be remembered no more' (Zechariah 13:2)—there will be no consequences of obesity or excess weight in that land to come and no slimming clubs! A bride will want to look after herself so that, on her wedding day, she will be in her best possible shape. Likewise, there is the anticipation that we develop the proper mindset as we wait to meet Christ, our heavenly bridegroom, by looking after ourselves with the resources that He has given.

ACTION POINTS

- *Put the sin of gluttony to death and ask for forgiveness from God*

- *Give your body back to God.*
- *Let the Holy Spirit rule in your whole body.*

NOTES

1 HW Perkins, 'Religious commitment, yuppy values, and well-being in post-collegiate life', *Review of Religious Research*, 32 (3), 244–51

2 Jason Todd, 'The Socially Acceptable Sin', *Relevant magazine*, 16 April 2018, https://relevantmagazine.com/god/socially-acceptable-sin/

3 Cited in: Joe McKeever, 'It's the Most Wonderful Sin of the Year', 16 December 2011, https://www.crosswalk.com/church/pastors-or-leadership/the-most-wonderful-sin-of-the-season.html

4 Justin Caba, 'Clergy members battle obesity: one-third of pastors in the US are obese', *Medical Daily*, 13 January 2015, https://www.medicaldaily.com/clergy-members-battle-obesity-one-third-pastors-us-are-obese-317616; 'Fat in Church', *Fox News*, 3 June 2012, https://www.foxnews.com/opinion/fat-in-church

5 Shannon McCoy, *HELP! I'm a Slave to Food*, Lifeline Minibooks, (Wapwallopen, Pennsylvania: Shepherd Press, 2014)

6 A McGrath, *Heresy: A History of Defending the Truth* (London: Harper Collins, 2009), pp. 121–122

7 M Reeves, The Breeze of the Centuries (Downers Grove, Illinois: IVP, 2010), p. 46

8 Tim Keller quoted in: Kelly Minter, *No Other Gods: Confronting our modern day idols* (Colorado Springs, Colorado: David C Cook Publishing Company, 2008), p. 27

9 Kevin DeYoung, 'The Attraction of Idolatry', The Gospel Coalition, 23 September 2016, https://www.thegospelcoalition.org/blogs/kevin-deyoung/the-attraction-of-idolatry/

10 John Calvin, *Institutes of the Christian Religion: 1536 edition* (Grand Rapids, Mississippi: Eerdmans, 1995), Section 4, Chapter 17, p. 36

11 Quoting Leviticus 26:12; Jeremiah 32:38; Ezekiel 37:27

12 Quoting Isaiah 52:11; Ezekiel 20:34, 41

13 Quoting 2 Samuel 7:14; 7:8

14 C S Lewis, *Mere Christianity* (New York: Macmillan, 1952), pp. 53–54

15 John Piper, 'How Can I Conquer Gluttony?' *Desiring God*, 2 January 2008, https://www.desiringgod.org/interviews/how-can-i-conquer-gluttony

16 Quoting Psalm 69:9

17 David Platt, *Counter Culture: A Compassionate Call to Counter Culture in a World of Poverty, Same-Sex Marriage, Racism, Sex Slavery, Immigration, Abortion, Persecution, Orphans, and Pornography* (Carol Stream, Illinois: Tyndale, 2015), pp. 160–161

18 J Scott McElroy, 'Are Christians thinking about their bodies all wrong? How to use your body for the glory of God', *Relevant Magazine*, 27 October 2017, https://relevantmagazine.com/article/christians-are-thinking-about-their-bodies-all-wrong-update/

19 Romans 12:5; 1 Corinthians 12:27; Ephesians 1:23; 4:12; Colossians 1:24; 2:19

20 Isaiah 62:5; Revelation 19:7; 21:2; 22:17

Conclusion

Dear children, keep yourselves from idols (1 John 5:21).

In conclusion, the dual sins of greed and idolatry are often seen in the outcomes of obesity and overweightness. These consequences in turn have many impacts—physically, mentally and spiritually.

Dr Ian Campbell, a family GP and obesity expert, exhorted: 'For many of us weight gain begins in early adult life, even childhood, and the cumulative effect of years of being slightly overweight means most of us are avoidably increasing our risk of life changing and life-shortening illnesses ... the time to start controlling our waistline, whatever our age, is now.'[1]

As a result of all these statistics, research and exhortations, we are urged to be in the best possible shape for the King. We are to be in good physical form so that we can serve Him here on earth, in the church community He has placed us with before He takes us to heaven in bodies that we cannot abuse or misuse.

In the end, it means coming to the cross and requesting forgiveness for the sin of gluttony that we have committed. We acknowledge that, on that instrument of death, Jesus gave His all for us, so we should give our all to Him, including the bodies that were created by Him and should be cared for by ourselves.

I would echo Paul's prayer for each of us: 'May God himself, the God of peace, sanctify you through and through. May your whole spirit, soul and body be kept blameless at the coming of our Lord Jesus Christ' (1 Thessalonians 5:23).

As I encourage you in your God-given desire to be healthy and active, let us also pray for ourselves and for others[2]:

> Lord, I pray that you will help me to truly see that my body is Your dwelling place. Enable me to protect my body through right choices in what I eat. Give me the motivation to exercise regularly so that I have endurance. Help me to get plenty of rest so that I am completely rejuvenated when I awaken. May I acknowledge You in all my ways— including the care of my body—so that You can direct my paths. Watch over me as I walk through my day and perform the tasks that demand my time and attention. Amen

NOTES

1   Giles Sheldrick, 'Diabetes News: Avoiding "middle-age spread" reduces risk of condition', *Daily Express*, 19 July 2017 https://www.express.co.uk/life-style/health/830267/Avoiding-middle-aged-spread-can-beat-diabetes

2   Adapted from: Stormie Omartian, *The Power of a Praying Husband—Book of Prayers* (Eugene, Oregon: Harvest House Publications, 2004), p. 96

Appendix A—
Body mass index (BMI)

BMI is not an exact science, but it can give an indication of whether you are overweight or obese.

The mathematics are that your weight in kilograms is divided by your height in metres, squared, so BMI = kg/m2.

To find out your own BMI please go to: shttps://bmicalculator.mes.fm/bmi-chart

The summary is as follows:
- BMI is less than 1.8   = underweight
- BMI is 18.5 to 25.0   = healthy
- BMI is 25.0 to 30.0   = overweight
- BMI is 30.0   = obese

It is to be noted that obesity has its own levels:
- Class 1: BMI of 30 to <35
- Class 2: BMI of 35 to <40
- Class 3: BMI of 40 or higher

However, it does not consider muscle mass, which may increase because of exercise.

The other deficit is that the chart does not account for the type of fat, which is important. Visceral fat that accumulates around the internal organs and results in bulging stomachs is proportionately more dangerous than subcutaneous fat, which is distributed around the body.

With these provisos, it is important that women are to keep their waist size below 35 inches and men are to see below 40 inches as the target.

Appendix B—
Blood pressure

What is blood pressure?

When the hearts beats, blood is pumped around the body. Blood carries essential elements and oxygen to the tissues. As the blood moves, it pushes against the walls of the blood vessels. The effort needed to pump blood around the body is termed 'blood pressure'.

If the blood pressure is too high, it puts extra strain on the arteries and the heart, which may result in a heart attack or a stroke (the latter is commonly known as Cerebrovascular Accident or CVA).

What is normal blood pressure?

Ideally, the blood pressure should be less than 120 over 80 (120/80) for people of good health. This rate greatly lowers the risk of heart disease or stroke.

What do the numbers mean?

Every blood pressure reading consists of two numbers or levels. They are shown as one number over another.

The first (or top) number is the *systolic* blood pressure. It is the highest level the blood pressure reaches when the heart beats.

The second (or bottom) number is the *diastolic* blood pressure. It is the lowest level the blood pressure reaches as the heart relaxes between beats.

Blood Pressure Chart

Blood Pressure Category	Systolic Mm Hg (upper #)		Diastolic Mm Hg (lower #)
Hypotension	Less than 90	or	Less than 60
Normal	Less than 120	and	Less than 80
Prehypertension	120–139	or	80–89
High Blood Pressure (Hypertension) Stage 1	140–159	or	90–99
High Blood Pressure (Hypertension) Stage 2	160 or higher	or	100 or higher
Hypertensive Crisis (Emergency care needed)	Higher than 180	or	Higher than 110

The blood pressure chart is suitable for adults of any age as the level for high blood pressure does not change with age.

What blood pressure readings mean

As observed on the blood pressure chart, *only one of the numbers has to be higher or lower than it should be* to count as either high blood pressure or low blood pressure.

Keeping blood pressure at the optimum level

Even if you do not have high blood pressure at the moment, it is important to monitor it and keep your blood pressure at the optimum level for continued good health. The higher the blood pressure, the higher the risk of health problems.

How you can tell if blood pressure is high

Having high blood pressure (hypertension) is not usually something that a person feels or notices. It does not tend to produce obvious signs or symptoms. The only definitive way to know if you have high pressure is by having it taken and recorded.

Electronic blood pressure machines can be obtained at pharmacists or on reputable websites. The instructions must be followed carefully. The equipment needs to be 'clinically calibrated' and then further re-calibrated at least once every two years to ensure that accurate results are obtained.

Hypotension – Low Blood Pressure

As long as symptoms of low blood pressure are not being experienced, there is no need for concern. Most doctors consider chronically low blood pressure as being dangerous only if there are noticeable signs and symptoms such as:

- Dizziness or light headedness
- Fainting
- Dehydration and unusual thirst (dehydration can sometimes cause blood pressure to drop, but it does not automatically mean there is low blood pressure)
- Lack of concentration
- Blurred vision
- Nausea

If no symptoms are present, low blood pressure will not be a problem. However, if blood pressure is normally higher or if any of the symptoms listed above are experienced, a low blood pressure may have an underlying cause.

A GP or Nurse Practitioner may request your blood pressure is monitored if they think there is a need for regular checks.

Appendix C— Ordinary walking revitalised

The table contains a calorie breakdown based both on your weight and the type of walking you are doing.[1]

If you weigh between 120–140 pounds

WALKING AT A MODERATE PACE (3 MPH [MILES PER HOUR])
- 15 minutes: 50 calories
- 30 minutes: 100 calories
- 1 hour: 200 calories

WALKING AT A FAST PACE (4–5 MPH)
- 15 minutes: 95 calories
- 30 minutes: 185 calories
- 1 hour: 370 calories

WALKING UPHILL (3.5 MPH)
- 15 minutes: 90 calories
- 30 minutes: 180 calories
- 1 hour: 355 calories

WALKING UP STAIRS (3 MPH)
- 15 minutes: 120 calories
- 30 minutes: 240 calories
- 1 hour: 275 calories

WALKING DOWNHILL (2.5 MPH)
- 15 minutes: 40 calories

- 30 minutes: 85 calories
- 1 hour: 165 calories

If you weigh between 140 – 160 pounds

WALKING AT A MODERATE PACE (3 MPH)

- 15 minutes: 60 calories
- 30 minutes: 112 calories
- 1 hour: 225 calories

WALKING AT A FAST PACE (4–5 MPH)

- 15 minutes: 100 calories
- 30 minutes: 214 calories
- 1 hour: 430 calories

WALKING UPHILL (3.5 MPH)

- 15 minutes: 102 calories
- 30 minutes: 204 calories
- 1 hour: 408 calories

WALKING UP STAIRS (3 MPH)

- 15 minutes: 130 calories
- 30 minutes: 275 calories
- 1 hour: 545 calories

WALKING DOWNHILL (2.5 MPH)

- 15 minutes: 50 calories
- 30 minutes: 95 calories
- 1 hour: 190 calories

If you weigh between 160–180 pounds

WALKING AT A MODERATE PACE (3 MPH)

- 15 minutes: 65 calories
- 30 minutes: 127 calories
- 1 hour: 255 calories

WALKING AT A FAST PACE (4–5 MPH)

- 15 minutes: 120 calories
- 30 minutes: 245 calories
- 1 hour: 485 calories

WALKING UPHILL (3.5 MPH)

- 15 minutes: 115 calories
- 30 minutes: 230 calories
- 1 hour: 485 calories

WALKING UP STAIRS (3 MPH)

- 15 minutes: 155 calories
- 30 minutes: 310 calories
- 1 hour: 620 calories

WALKING DOWNHILL (2.5 MPH)

- 15 minutes: 54 calories
- 30 minutes: 110 calories
- 1 hour: 215 calories

There are other ways in which you can dispose of more calories:

- Adding weights to your ankles or arms (such as carrying a heavier water bottle).

- Switching between the different categories mentioned above to keep things interesting.
- Having a breather to do other forms of exercise (such as squats, lunges, planks and push-ups) before continuing on the walk.

NOTES

1 I was alerted to this content in: Tehrene Firman, 'This is exactly how many calories you burn from walking', *Good Housekeeping*, 8 August 2018, https://www.goodhousekeeping.com/health/fitness/a47008/calories-burned-from-walking/

Acknowledgements

There have been numerous people who have encouraged me in the writing of this book on the subject of obesity and excess weight from a Christian perspective, both in how it affects us in so many ways and also how it impacts on the wider world. The list of encouragers would be too long to include here.

I thank all those who have read the drafts, prayed for the book and prompted me in my thinking. In particular, I have appreciated the insights of Jonathan Martin and the medical knowledge of Sharon Conibeer, two close friends.

I also thank Mark Roberts and the team at Day One for facilitating the publication of this book. I give my special thanks to Helen Clark, a unique editor who has provided clinical knowledge and made the words run smoother than they would have done otherwise—I admire you for your patience.

My parents, Colin and Jean, have provided me with the concern for other people and wanting to make the world more as God would want it.

Lastly in this list, but definitely the most important, I thank my wife Deborah for her encouragements, prayers and enthusiasm for this book.

Above all, I thank God who has provided all that is good in this world and wants us to enjoy it in a responsible manner.